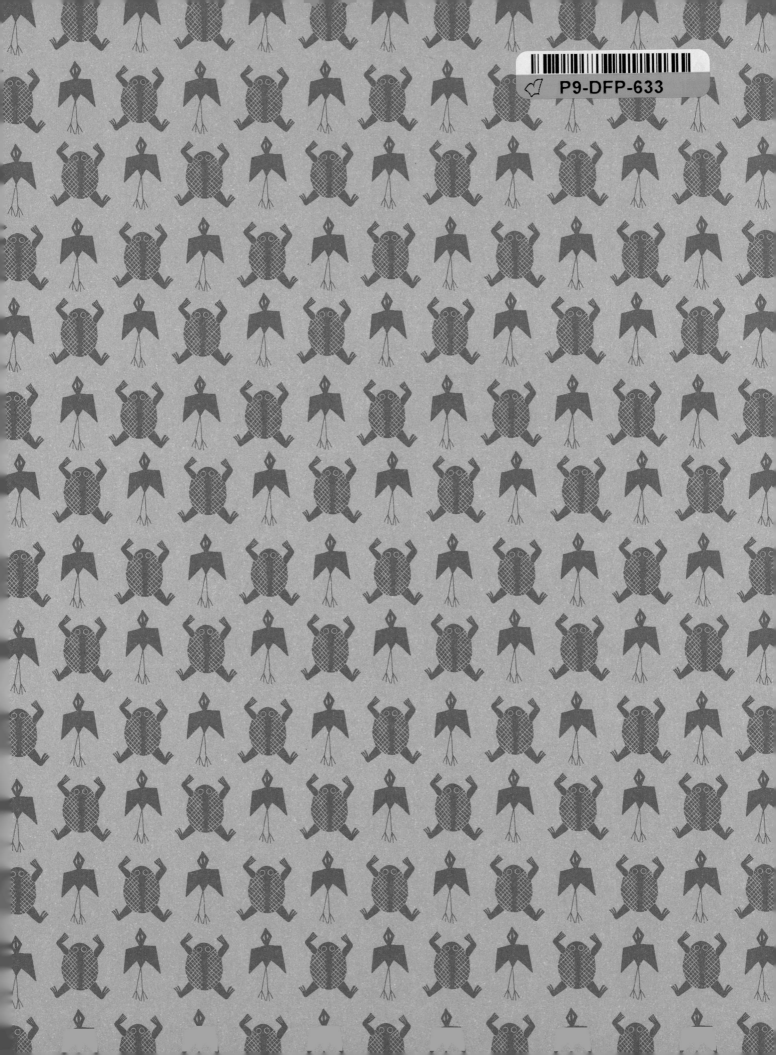

AFRICAN

FOLKTALES

Retold by A. Ceni

Illustrations by Lorena Chiuppi

BARNES
&NOBLE
BOOKS
NEW YORK

Originally published as *Fiabe Africane* by Bulgarini Publishing, 1991

English language edition copyright © 1998 by Barnes & Noble, Inc.

This edition published by Barnes & Noble, Inc.,
by arrangement with Bulgarini Publishing

1998 Barnes & Noble Books

English translation by Elizabeth Leister

Illustrations by Lorena Chiuppi, M.I.A.

Text design for original Italian-language edition
by Lorena Chiuppi, M.I.A.

Cover and text design for English-language edition by Leah Lococo

ISBN 0-7607-0857-6

Printed and bound in Spain

98 99 00 01 M 9 8 7 6 5 4 3 2 1

Gráficas

Contents

The Greatest Warrior of All

 MASAI

Once upon a time, just out of curiosity, a caterpillar slipped into a hare's den: Seeing that there was nobody there, he made himself right at home in the darkest and most sheltered corner of the cool den. After a while, the hare came back and when he saw the tracks on the ground, he was most astonished.

"Whoever can this creature be who leaves these little marks in the dust?" he thought.

Unable to get to the bottom of the mystery, he asked in a loud voice:

"Who is in my house?"

The caterpillar, who was something of a braggart, answered:

"I am the greatest warrior of all! I smash the rhinoceros to the ground and I make mincemeat out of the elephant! I am truly terrible!"

Hearing these words, the hare trembled with fear and took to his heels.

"By the Sacred Forest," he thought, "what can I do against someone who says that he is the greatest warrior of all?"

As he was running away, he met up with the jackal on the pathway.

"Brother jackal," he said, "would you mind helping me?"

"With pleasure, if I can," the jackal replied.

"Come to my house and *you* try to talk to the so-and-so who has set himself up in there."

The jackal agreed and when the two animals reached the entrance to the den, the jackal shouted at the top of his voice:

"Who is hiding in my friend the hare's house?"

The caterpillar was not at all worried, and he replied:

"I am not hiding. I am the greatest of all warriors! I smash the rhinoceros to the ground and I make mincemeat out of the elephant! I am truly terrible!"

The jackal completely lost his courage and, apologizing to the hare, he said that with a little so-and-so like that he could do very little indeed. He said good-bye, and ran off.

The bitterly disappointed hare retraced his steps and went to look for the leopard. He found the leopard under a tree and made the same request of him: Could he go and see who on earth has set himself up in his house?

The leopard didn't waste any time, and when he got to the entrance to the hare's den he said in a loud voice:

"Who is hiding in my friend the hare's house?"

And once again, the caterpillar was not frightened, and he promptly responded:

"I am not hiding. I am the greatest of all warriors! I smash the rhinoceros to the ground and I make mincemeat out of the elephant! I am truly terrible!"

The leopard was quite puzzled. He looked at the hare and said to him:

"My dear hare, if this creature is able to do all that, I don't see how I could come out of this with my life, even if I am the great leopard. I'm sorry, but it's better if I just leave."

The hare began to give up hope. He thought and he thought, and finally he decided that the only thing to do was to turn to the very animals invoked by the terrible warrior.

So he went to see the rhinoceros and told him the whole story. The large beast, who took great pride in his strength and in his horn, followed the hare to his den and bellowed in a menacing voice:

"Who are you who dares to hide in the house of my friend the hare?"

And in a voice amplified by the hole in the ground so that it seemed like the voice of a giant, the caterpillar replied:

"I am not hiding. Come on in, if you have the nerve! But don't forget, rhinoceros, that I am the greatest of all warriors and I smash to the ground any rhinoceros that I run into!"

The rhinoceros was dumbfounded by this answer. He thought it over, and then said to the hare:

"He said 'smash to the ground,' huh? Well, I'm sure that he's just boasting, but . . . anyway . . . maybe it's better to forget about it. Take care of yourself, my dear hare!" And he took off at a good trot.

The poor little hare then went to see the elephant.

"Oh, great elephant, second only to the king, the lion, please help me! There is a terrible warrior in my den who has thoroughly abused the rhinoceros and who says that he can make mincemeat out of you!"

The elephant scratched his head with his enormous trunk, flapped his immense ears a bit, and fidgeted somewhat uneasily. Finally, he cleared his throat and said:

"My dear hare, I would be very interested in taking on your terrible warrior . . . but it just happens to be almost bath time and I can't pass that up. And don't look for me tomorrow either: I'm leaving. See you soon, my friend!" Then he turned around and with a bouncy gait that one would not have expected from such a stately animal, he moved deeper into the forest.

The hare was truly desperate. He sat down on the grass and began to sigh heavily. After a while, a frog passed through the meadow, and seeing the hare in such an unhappy state, he stopped and asked him:

"My dear hare, why such great sighs? What is the matter with you?"

"If you only knew, . . ." the hare responded between sighs, "my house has been occupied by the greatest of all warriors, a terrible monster. Just imagine, he has driven off the jackal, the leopard, the rhinoceros, and even the elephant without even leaving my den! So that is the state I find myself in!"

"There, there, it seems incredible," said the frog.

"If only it were! He is a warrior who smashes rhinoceroses to the ground and makes mincemeat out of elephants, and he's not kidding!"

"That certainly makes me want to go and see what an ugly puss he must have," said the frog, and without wasting any more time, he headed toward the hare's house, moving in great, long leaps.

When the frog reached the den, he stood in the entryway and cried out:

"Who is hiding in my friend the hare's house?"

And the caterpillar, who had developed quite a swelled head after having driven off the jackal, the leopard, the rhinoceros, and the elephant, answered in the same booming voice as before:

"I am not hiding. I am the greatest of all warriors! I have made all of the animals of

the savannas and of the forest run away! I smashed the rhinoceros to the ground and I made mincemeat out of the elephant!"

The frog, who, as everybody well knows, is as brave and intelligent as he is ugly, didn't take these words too seriously and, with a great leap, he entered the den.

"Where are you?" said the frog as he advanced into the darkness. "I am really happy to have found an adversary who is worthy of me."

Then the caterpillar saw the frog, with his big green, green head and his yellow, yellow eyes, drawing near, and the caterpillar was afraid. Hiding himself in a corner at the back of the den, he whispered weakly:

"It's just the caterpillar."

The frog smiled, picked up the caterpillar, and carried him outside. The hare was a bit ashamed, but he quickly cheered up when he thought about how the animals he had gone to for help had behaved: They were big, strong, and scared.

"A thousand thanks, my friend the frog," said the hare. "You, who everybody teases for being ugly, you, a small, defenseless animal, were the bravest and cleverest of us all and I will tell the world of your deed!"

While the hare was saying this, all of the animals of the plains and of the forest had drawn near the hare's den, attracted by the great to-do. And you can imagine the laugh they had when the hare explained how it had all turned out.

The Daughter of the Sun and the Moon

 MBUNDU

Once upon a time, there lived a handsome and brave young man named Kia-Tumba Ndala, the son of the chieftain Kimanaueze, and all of the girls wanted him for their husband. Kimanaueze also wanted his son to marry, and more and more often he said to Kia:

"My son, it is now time for you to take a wife and start a family. Look around at the girls in the village and pick the one that pleases you most."

But every time, Kia-Tumba Ndala had some excuse at hand, or even pretended not to hear his father. Finally one day, after his father's umpteenth request, Kia answered:

"I don't want a woman of the Earth for my wife."

Kimanaueze thought that he had not understood and asked:

"What did you say? Who do you want to marry?"

"I said," answered Kia, somewhat impatiently, "that I don't want a woman of the Earth for my wife."

"And who else would you want to marry?" answered his father, even more astonished.

"If I really have to marry, then I want the daughter of the Sun and the Moon for my wife."

"Be reasonable, my son. How can we possibly go up to heaven and ask for the hand of the daughter of the Sun and the Moon?"

"We'll see! But in the meantime, I'm telling you that I will marry no other."

The whole village thought that the young man had fallen under some kind of spell that had clouded his wits, and even his father stopped talking to him about marriage.

But Kia-Tumba was more than determined in his intention, and he wrote a proposal of marriage addressed to the Sun in which he solemnly asked for his daughter's hand.

Letter in hand, he went to see Deer so that he could carry it up to heaven, but Deer shook his head no, and said:

"I can't go all the way up there!"

Kia-Tumba then went to see Antelope, but she also said to him:

9

"I can't go all the way up to heaven!"

Then Kia-Tumba went to see Hawk, but he spread his wings wide and said:

"I can fly all right, but I can't go as far as the Sun!"

Finally he went to see Vulture, but even Vulture answered:

"I can manage to make it halfway there, but all the way up there, all the way up to heaven, no, I just can't make it!"

At that point, the young man felt quite discouraged and thought that this marriage really was impossible: He went back into his hut, shut the letter up in a box, and tried not to think about it anymore.

But at this point, you need to know that Lord Sun and Lady Moon's slave girls were in the habit of coming to draw water from a well located near Kia-Tumba's village, and that Frog, who lived right nearby, had caught them at it more than once.

One day, Frog, who had heard about Kia-Tumba's idea, and who was eager to make himself useful, went to look for Kia.

"I know that you have written a proposal of marriage," said Frog.

"Yes, I wrote it. But it's as if I hadn't: There isn't anybody who can bring it up to heaven."

"Give me the letter, and I'll take care of it."

"Don't be silly!" exclaimed Kia, amused in spite of himself. "How can you go all the way up to heaven when even the animals with wings aren't able to?"

But Frog answered him:

"Trust me, I know what I'm saying!"

Kia-Tumba thought it over for a little while, but seeing that he didn't have anything to lose anyway, he gave the letter to Frog, adding:

"Bear in mind that if you don't succeed in delivering the letter, I'll see that you regret it."

Frog wasn't overly worried, and he went off to the well where Lord Sun and Lady Moon's slave girls went to draw water. He put the letter in his mouth, jumped in the water, and oh so quietly, and without moving a muscle, he settled himself down to wait.

Not much time passed before the slave girls arrived: They lowered a jug into the well, and Frog quickly jumped into it; the jug filled with water, and the slave girls hauled it back up. No one noticed Frog, and in the twinkling of an eye, they flew up to heaven. Once inside Lord Sun's house, they put the jug in its place and went away.

At that point, Frog jumped out of the container, leapt up onto a large table that stood in the middle of the room, put the letter down on the table, and then ever so quickly hid himself in a dark corner.

After a little while, Lord Sun came in to look for something to drink. He cast a glance at the table, and saw the letter. Then he summoned the slave girls and asked:

"And this, where did this come from?"

"Master, we really don't know!" they answered.

So Lord Sun took up a paper knife, opened the letter, and read it.

"I, Kia-Tumba Ndala, son of Kimanaueze, a man from the Earth, wish to take the daughter of Lord Sun and Lady Moon for my wife."

Lord Sun smiled to himself and thought, "But just look at the ideas the Earth people come up with! Brave, though, this Kia. But who could have brought the message?"

Lord Sun didn't say anything; he just put the letter in his pocket and went out.

Meanwhile, the slave girls were going to go back to the well to fetch more water. So Frog jumped back into the jug without anybody noticing him, and went back down to Earth with them. And immediately he set off for the village.

When he reached Kia-Tumba's hut, he knocked on the door, and as soon as the young man saw Frog, he asked him:

"My dear Frog, have you come to tell me that you've delivered the letter, or have you come to get your beating?"

"I have indeed delivered the letter, and so spare yourself the trouble!" answered Frog.

"If that is so, then why don't you have an answer?" insisted Kia.

"This I do not know," said Frog. "But I do know that the right person read it, and if you want to, you can write another message, pressing for an answer; I'm willing to go back up to heaven to help you."

Kia-Tumba hesitated for a moment because he was afraid that Frog was making fun of him; but at last the thought of the daughter of the Sun and the Moon returned to warm his heart, and he decided to make another attempt. He sat down at the table and wrote:

"I, Kia-Tumba Ndala, son of Kimanaueze, a man from the Earth, have already written to you, Lord Sun and Lady Moon, to ask for your daughter's hand in marriage. The letter was delivered, but I have not received a reply. Therefore, I am sending you this new letter in order to find out if my proposal is agreeable to you or not."

He signed the letter, folded it up, sealed it, and handed it over to Frog who set off once again for the well. When Frog arrived at the well, he jumped in and waited for the slave girls to come to draw water. Not long afterward, he was once again in heaven in Lord Sun's chamber. He jumped out of the jug, left Kia-Tumba's letter in plain sight on the table, and went to hide in the same dark little corner.

And not long afterward, there was Lord Sun, entering the room; he saw the letter on the table; he opened it and read it. His amazement grew and he immediately summoned the slave girls to ask for an explanation.

"My dear girls," he said, "seeing that you are always going down to Earth to fetch water, could you by chance be the ones who are bringing these letters?"

But the slave girls, even more amazed than their master, responded:

"No sir, we really have nothing to do with this matter."

Perplexed, Lord Sun scratched his head, unable to figure out how these letters had reached him. Nevertheless, he took a sheet of paper and wrote:

"You have been sending me letters, how I don't know, in which you say that you want my daughter for your wife. Now listen: I give you my consent on the condition that you come here in person with your first gift, so that I can see what kind of a man you are."

He signed, folded, and sealed the letter. Then he placed it on the table and left the room.

Then Frog sprang out of his dark corner, jumped up on the table, took the letter, hid himself in a jug, and when the girls went back to Earth to draw water, they brought him with them to the well. There, as before, he waited until the slave girls had disappeared into the heavens, then he came out and went to the village.

He arrived at Kia's hut, knocked, said hello, and delivered Lord Sun's answer. Kia couldn't believe his eyes.

"So you were telling me the truth!" he exclaimed, utterly happy. "I will prepare the first gift right away so that you can take it to Lord Sun."

He took a leather bag, filled it with forty jingling coins, and wrote another letter in which he said:

"Dear Lord Sun and Lady Moon, this is my first gift. I cannot come to you because I have to stay on Earth to organize the wedding ceremony."

And Frog, using his usual system, went back up to heaven, left the purse with the money in it on the table, and in the same way as he got there, he went back.

And so, for some time, Frog continued to carry messages from Earth to heaven and from heaven to Earth, along with the future husband's gifts and the future in-laws' regards.

Day by day, a month passed, and then another, and finally the moment arrived to set the wedding date. But Kia-Tumba couldn't make up his mind because he was very worried. For twelve days he couldn't sleep a wink; finally he summoned Frog and confided his predicament to him:

"My friend, I cannot go to heaven, nor do I know anybody capable of going all the way up there to fetch my bride. What shall I do?"

"But there's me!" protested Frog. "*I'll* go, as always, and I'll find a way to bring the girl back here. Don't worry."

"And how can you do something like that when you're so little?" responded Kia-Tumba, inconsolable. "Thanks for the thought, maybe another time."

But Frog insisted:

"Don't worry, don't worry! You will see that I will find a way." And with this, he went on his way.

He went back to the well and jumped inside; he waited until the slave girls came to draw water; then he jumped into a jug and was carried up to heaven. There, he hid himself in his usual corner in the usual room.

The time came when even Lord Sun went to bed; everything grew dark and silent. Frog came out of his hiding place and went to look for the beautiful daughter of the Sun and the Moon. He searched and searched until he found her, sound asleep in her bed. He quietly went up to the pillow, took out a needle and thread, and began to sew up the eyelids of the sleeping beauty.

Of course, they were a magic needle and thread that, as well as being invisible, didn't hurt at all; the result, however, was that once her eyelids were sewn together, no one could lift them up.

So when the girl woke up the next morning, she couldn't open her eyes. Frightened, she immediately began to cry for help.

"What is the matter, my dear daughter?" asked Lady Moon, running into the room.

"Mama, Mama! It's as if I have a terrible weight on my eyes! I can't open them, and I'm afraid that I've gone blind!"

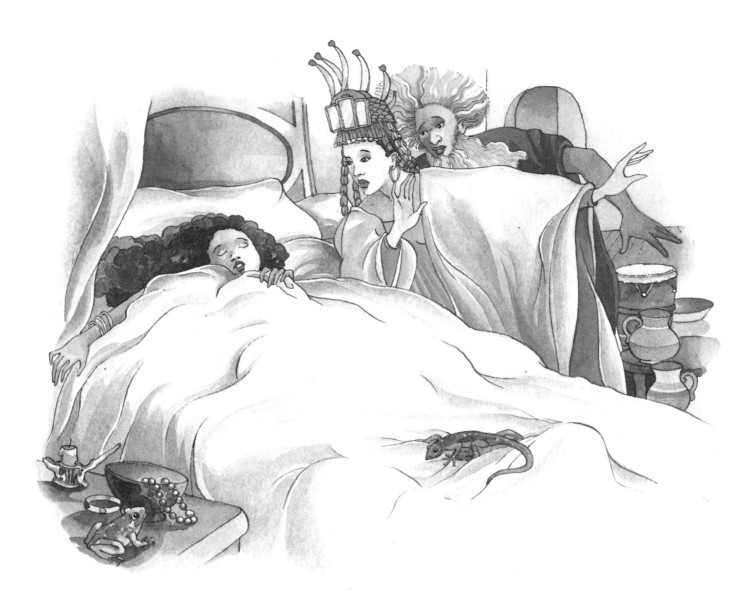

Lord Sun also came in at a run, and after looking at his daughter's closed eyes, he said:

"Everything seems to be in order, but an extraordinary force is holding them down! What could it be? Perhaps some spell, because yesterday the child was fine!"

"What can we do?" Lady Moon asked, weeping silver tears.

"I shall send two messengers to the wise witch doctor Ngombo; he will be able to advise us," answered the blazing Sun. And summoning two slaves, he sent them down to Earth.

Frog, who had heard everything, leapt into one of the jugs, and using the usual method, in a very short while found himself back home again. He immediately set off for the hut of the witch doctor Ngombo, arriving before the two messengers who had tarried along the way, enticed by a mulberry bush. Taking advantage of the fact that the witch

doctor had gone out on some business of his own, Frog went into the house, barred the door, and got himself under the ceremonial mask that hung on the wall.

A little while later, Lord Sun's two slaves knocked at the door:

"Who is it? Who's there?" asked Frog from behind the mask, and his voice resounded throughout the hut.

The two identified themselves and asked if they could come in. But Frog answered:

"Impossible, I'm too busy. Tell me from out there what Lord Sun wants from me."

The messengers did not insist, and told him what had happened to their master's daughter. Frog listened in perfect silence, as if he were very interested, allowed a few minutes to pass to give the impression of being immersed in goodness knows what thoughts, and finally, in the same big voice, he said:

"Without a doubt, the girl has become ill because her bridegroom cannot go up to her in heaven and fetch her. It is a spell that everybody knows, very old and very powerful. It says: 'Daughter of the Sun and the Moon come quickly to me, else night shall fall on you forever.' Messengers, go in haste, and tell your Lord her father that he should immediately send the girl to Earth: There is no other way to escape death."

The slaves went back and told their master what the witch doctor Ngombo had said, while Frog rushed to Kia-Tumba's village.

"Kia-Tumba! Kia-Tumba!" cried Frog. "Get ready! Your bride will be here this very day!"

The young man came to the door and sadly asked:

"And how can that be possible? You are trying to pull my leg, Frog. Go away, don't lie to me!"

"But you must believe what I'm saying," answered Frog. "You will see that before this evening your future bride will be here." And without giving Kia the time to reply, Frog went back to the well, plunged into the water, and began to wait.

In fact, as Frog had foreseen, the Sun had really gotten down to business as soon as the two messengers had told him how things stood. He had immediately ordered Spider to weave a long, sturdy web on which his poor blind daughter could descend to Earth.

And lo and behold, toward sundown, the spiderweb was let down from heaven, and the beautiful daughter of the Sun descended to Earth accompanied by her slave girls. The young women settled the girl near the well, combed her hair, comforted her, and begged her to wait there quietly; then they turned around and went back to heaven.

As soon as the daughter of the Sun was alone, Frog came out of the water, and drawing near to her, he said:

"Don't be afraid. I will heal you and take you to your future husband."

He took a little magic knife and began to cut the thread that only he could see. When the operation was over, the girl could see again, and together, the two headed off for the village.

They arrived in front of Kia-Tumba's hut, and Frog knocked on the door.

"Here is your bride!" he exclaimed as soon as Kia opened the door.

The young man was astonished by the girl's beauty and stood there speechless, while Frog, who did not like to be thanked, took advantage of the moment to disappear without catching anyone's eye.

The son of the Earth married the daughter of the Sun and the Moon, and they lived happily ever after.

The Number Eleven Child

 ASHANTI

Once upon a time, there was a stepmother who had eleven children. As we all know, a child is often hungry; just imagine what it was like with eleven of them! As long as her husband, who was a great hunter, was alive, the morning and evening meals were guaranteed. But one day her husband died, and so the stepmother, who had never loved those children who were not her own, had to see to it that those constantly hungry children did not go hungry all by herself.

For a little while, she tried hard to give them something to eat at least once a day, but in a little while she had had enough, and she began to think about how to put an end to this nasty state of affairs.

So she decided to go into the farm field behind her house and speak to the breadfruit tree.

"My dear tree," she said, "do me a favor and you will have water even during the drought. In a moment, I am going to send my eleven stepsons to gather pumpkins. As soon as they are in range, make your biggest fruit fall down on their heads and kill them."

And the breadfruit tree answered:

"Agreed. For the water you have promised me, I will do you this favor."

The stepmother went back home, called the children, and said to them:

"Go into the field behind the house and gather the ripe pumpkins under the breadfruit tree. Bring them to me so I can cook them for you."

The children walked up to the breadfruit tree, but Number Eleven, the youngest of them all, who the day before had heard their stepmother mumbling to herself about what she would like to do to get rid of her stepsons, stopped his brothers and said:

"Do you know why our stepmother has sent us under the breadfruit tree to gather pumpkins?"

And his brothers answered:

"So that she can cook them and we can eat them."

"Not at all!" retorted Number Eleven. "She asked this tree to make its biggest fruits fall on our heads to get rid of us. But we will fool it: Each of you take a nice big stone and throw it at the tree."

And so that's what they did; and the breadfruit tree, thinking that the children had come, dropped eleven big fruits. Then Number Eleven said:

"Brothers, did you see? If we had been under there, we would already be dead."

They gathered the pumpkins and the breadfruit, and brought them to their step-mother as if nothing had happened. She was amazed at this, but she couldn't say a thing. On the contrary, she was forced to cook the pumpkins and serve the fruits for dinner.

The stepmother let a little time pass, but one day she decided to apply directly to the spirit-of-the-sky. She went to see him and said:

"Spirit, help me. My stepchildren are ruining me: They do nothing but eat and they are never full. I beg you, catch these children and make them disappear. I will repay you with great offerings."

The spirit-of-the-sky hesitated for a little while, but finally he gave in. He summoned a couple of his servants and ordered them to dig a pit and fill it with sharp pieces of broken bottles. He himself added a whole nest of serpents and then had the pit covered with leaves and branches. He then sent the two servants to summon the brothers.

All unsuspecting, the children went, but when they neared the pit, Number Eleven, who had noticed the turned soil and the freshly cut branches, told his brothers to go through the woods instead of along the road.

The brothers were surprised and asked:

"But why go through the woods when there's a road?"

Number Eleven responded:

"One of you throw your stick a little bit ahead of us where those cut branches are."

Number Ten, who was the closest, threw his stick that immediately sank into the pit. Then they all approached the trap and saw the pieces of broken bottles and the serpents. And Number Eleven commented:

"You see? This is what would have happened to us if we had continued along the road."

So they chose a path through the woods and set off on their way again. After half a day, they finally arrived at the abode of the spirit-of-the-sky, who was more than a little surprised to see them safe and sound, but who had also provided for this possibility. In fact, he had prepared eleven pits in each of which he had imprisoned a leopard. He had then covered the pits with a layer of rushes on which he had then placed a comfortable stool: If the children got as far as his place, he would invite them to sit down and rest up from their trip, and thus they would fall into the traps. Indeed, as soon as he saw them, the spirit-of-the-sky said:

"Oh, you poor little things! Goodness knows how tired you must be! But see, over there are some comfortable stools for you—sit and rest!"

Number Eleven didn't like the sound of that "for you" at all, and he said:

"You've gone to too much trouble, sir. We are merely poor children, and the

stools that you have made ready for us are worthy of kings. Thank you, but we prefer to sit under this tree."

The spirit-of-the-sky didn't know what to say, and was forced to put them up for the night.

The next morning, the spirit-of-the-sky had it in mind to get rid of the nuisance created by the stepmother and send the children to Death herself. So he called them and said:

"Children, I have asked you to come to me because I am certain that only you can help me. Please do me the favor of going to the old woman who lives at the end of this big road, near the dry riverbed: She has had a debt to settle with me for some time now. Don't tell her that I'm the one who sent you, but try to get her to give you a gold pipe, a gold toothpick, a gold snuffbox, a gold bell, and a gold flyswatter. I'm sure that you will succeed."

Then Number Eleven said, "Spirit-of-the-sky, you are a powerful lord who should be honored and feared: Providing you this small service will be a pleasure for us!"

And the little brothers lined themselves up and walked along the big road toward the

dried-up riverbed. But as they came within sight of the hut, Number Eleven made everybody stop as he usually did. He looked around and said:

"My dear brothers, this is not the house of an ordinary old woman; Death lives here. She is the only creature on Earth who can live beside a river that is always dry, because she never needs to drink."

The children were frightened and said that they wanted to turn back right away, but Number Eleven spoke again:

"Don't be afraid, just leave things to me. Let's see if we can succeed in changing misfortune into fortune."

So they went forward and knocked at the door of the hut. From inside, Death said:

"Nobody ever comes here; no one has the courage to pay me a visit. You who are knocking, why are you here?"

The eleven answered in chorus, "We were taking a walk in the woods and we got lost!"

"Oh really? Then do come in," responded Death.

Now you need to know that Death had ten sons. So when night fell, Death gave one of the children to each of her sons so that they could sleep two-by-two in the ten little beds; she took Number Eleven with her and went off to bed.

In the dead of night, Death touched Number Eleven with her hand to see if he had fallen asleep, so she could eat him up in her own sweet time.

But Number Eleven was not asleep at all and he immediately said:

"Granny, I'm not asleep yet!"

"And when will you fall asleep?" asked Death.

"Maybe I'll be able to fall asleep if I first smoke your gold pipe for a little while," answered Number Eleven.

So Death got out of bed, rummaged around in her trunk, and brought him the gold pipe. A little bit of time passed, and Death again touched Number Eleven to see if he had fallen asleep.

"Granny, I'm not asleep yet!"

"And when will you fall asleep?" asked Death.

"If you bring me the gold snuffbox, maybe then I'll be able to fall asleep!" answered Number Eleven.

Death got out of bed, rummaged around in the trunk, and brought him the gold snuffbox. A little more time passed, and again Death touched the little boy to see if he had fallen asleep.

"Granny, I'm not asleep yet!"

"And when will you fall asleep?" replied Death.

"Maybe if you let me chew on a gold toothpick I'll fall asleep!"

Death got out of bed, rummaged around in the trunk, and brought him the gold toothpick.

Some more time passed, and Death again touched Number Eleven to see if he had fallen asleep.

"Granny, I'm not asleep yet!"

"And when will you fall asleep?" asked Death.

"If you bring me a gold bell, maybe I'll be able to sleep!" said Number Eleven.

Death got out of bed again, rummaged around in the trunk again, and brought him the gold bell. Another little bit of time passed, and Death again touched Number Eleven to see if he had fallen asleep.

"Oh, Granny," the little boy insisted, "there's nothing to be done about it, I'm still not asleep!"

And Death, beginning to lose her patience, said:

"But you just have to make up your mind to do it!"

"Maybe," went on Number Eleven, "if you go to that lake over there, the one way far away where the first people's huts are, and if you get me some water in a strainer so I can quench this awful thirst, maybe I will be able to fall asleep."

Death, who was not exactly renowned for her intelligence, quickly snatched up a strainer and went to the lake, over there, way far away. She began to draw the water, but the strainer wouldn't retain the least little bit of it. In the meantime, Number Eleven had very quietly gone up to each of his brothers and awakened him, saying:

"Quick, get up and run away."

One by one, they were all on their feet, and one by one they crossed the threshold of the house and ran away down the road. Number Eleven went out into the farmyard, cut a few nice branches off the banana tree, went back inside, and arranged the branches in the beds beside Death's soundly sleeping children, completely covering the branches with the blankets; then he sat down to wait for Death to return.

Meanwhile, Death continued to draw water with the strainer, and an hour had already gone by in this useless endeavor, when who should pass by but her friend Funeral, who was just that moment returning from one of his services in the village of men. Funeral saw Death and asked her:

"And what might you be doing, my friend?"

"I'm drawing holes in the water with the colander," she replied, completely confused.

"What are you doing? What did you say?" demanded Funeral.

"Oh, it's much too long a story! Listen, for the whole night, a little bit of a kid has managed to pull my leg. He has taken several gold objects away from me, and now he wants me to bring him some water in a strainer!"

"But have you gone mad?" exclaimed Funeral. "Plug up the holes in the strainer with some clay, and then draw the water, you fool!"

"You make me ashamed of myself, dear friend!" said Death, and then she did as he suggested. She finally collected the water and went back to her hut.

"Oh, Granny," said Number Eleven when he saw her, "thank you for the water, but now I'm hungry too; it will soon be dawn, and we need to make breakfast."

Death was too tired to answer, so she lit the fire and put the pot on. Then she went into the room where her children were sleeping, or so she thought, with Number Eleven's brothers. In the dark, she felt the bodies in each bed and strangled the one that seemed softer to her, thinking that it was one of the brothers. Of course, without realizing it, she killed all of her own children. "At least these," she thought, "won't get away anymore!" And she went back into the kitchen to make something to eat.

At last dawn broke, and Death, completely worn out, sat down by the fire. Number Eleven couldn't allow her to rest and so he said to her:

"Granny, a big ugly fly has landed on your back."

"Take one of those branches and swat it!" responded Death.

"Granny, you must be joking!" exclaimed Number Eleven. "A branch! I'm certain that a person of your standing must surely have a fine gold flyswatter in the house."

"Well, yes I do!" admitted Death, touched in her pride. "Go over there in the bedroom. You'll find it in the trunk."

The child went into the bedroom, got the flyswatter and went back to Death. But instead of killing the fly, he deliberately made it fly away. Then, pretending to be angry, he said:

"Oh no! Let it never be said that the big ugly fly that has dared to land on the back of this dear granny has gotten away unhurt! I will have no peace until I have caught it."

Pretending to chase the fly, he grabbed the golden objects he had tricked from Death, hid them in his satchel, and went outside waving the gold flyswatter, still pretending to chase the fly.

When he had gone a good bit away from Death's hut, Number Eleven stopped and shouted:

"Nyah, nyah, nyah, nyah, nyah, nyah! Hey you, Granny Death! I know what you are: You're a total fool! Not only have I robbed you of your gold, saved my brothers, and made you kill your own children, but now you've lost me too!"

"Ah, cursed traitor!" exploded Death. "I will hound you to the ends of the earth!"

And Number Eleven began to run away, and Death took off after him. He ran and ran until he reached the spot where his brothers had assembled at the foot of an enormous tree.

"Quick, brothers, everybody up to the top of the tree; Death is coming and she's not very happy!"

They all climbed up the tree just as Death arrived, all out of breath. She stopped, looked to the right, to the left, in front of her, in back of her, down, and up. And as soon as she lifted up her head, she saw the children.

"There you are, you scoundrels! Now nothing will save you!"—And she commenced: "You, little boy up there, *Kyere-he-ne!*"—and at that, a little boy suddenly fell out of the tree, stone cold. "*Kyere-he-ne!*"—and another one fell down. And on and on she went, ten times; at last only Number Eleven was left.

"*Kyere-he-ne!*" said Death again. But Number Eleven had already climbed down on the other side. Then Death scrambled to the top of the tree to see why on earth the last child had not fallen down.

"*Kyere-he-ne!*" said Number Eleven in his turn. "*Kyere-he-ne* to you, Death!" And Death fell down, stone cold: Even Death was dead now.

At this point, attracted by all the shouting, the spirit-of-the-sky arrived. At the sight of all those dead little children and of Number Eleven in tears, the spirit was moved, and he regretted in his heart that he had heeded the stepmother.

"Don't cry!" said the spirit-of-the-sky to Number Eleven. "Here, take this potion and sprinkle it on your brothers and they will come back to life."

Number Eleven splashed the magic liquid on his brothers' heads, and they immediately reopened their eyes, asking what had happened and why they were there.

Number Eleven, completely happy, was about to give back what remained of the potion to the spirit-of-the-sky when he tripped, and the contents of the vial spilled onto Death's head. And Death woke up again.

"Which of us is the fool this time?" she exclaimed, quite pleased, and she made to grab Number Eleven.

But the spirit-of-the-sky stopped her with a gesture and said:

"Hold! These children are under my protection. They will grow up and become hunters, warriors, and farmers. When their time arrives, come back and you will surely find them."

And thus it happened. Number Eleven and his ten brothers were free once more, and Death went off to ply her trade, but somewhere else.

The Toothless Pretty Maid

BAVENDA

Once upon a time, there was an old man who had three sons, all three of them still bachelors—an excusable state for the youngest who was little more than a lad, but the other two should have already had wives for some time now. And seeing as neither of the two gave the matter any thought, one day the father decided to take it into his own hands.

One fine morning, he went out and walked to the village to see if he could make a match for his eldest son. He spoke with the village chieftain who showed him a pretty maid of marriageable age. The father went back home, called his first-born son and said to him:

"I have found you a wife. Tomorrow you will go to her father and bring him three cows and two oxen as gifts."

The son did not object, and early in the morning of the next day, he walked to his future wife's village with the cattle for his future father-in-law. As soon as the young man arrived, he was welcomed with great ceremony, and the father of his betrothed said:

"Daughter, here is your bridegroom, go home with him!"

The girl seemed happy, and she followed the young man. But at a certain point along the way, the girl began to softly sing in the sweetest voice:

"Watch out, watch out, my handsome youth! I'm a pretty maid but I haven't a tooth!"

The young man became suspicious and said to her:

"Wait a minute, open your mouth and let's see if what you're saying is true."

The young maid stopped and opened her mouth; he looked inside and saw with great amazement that instead of teeth she just had two black lines.

"Good Lord! Nobody warned me about this flaw of yours. The marriage shall not take place, I will give you back to your father."

They went back, and the young man explained that he did not want a toothless wife, so he was taking back his cattle, and so long!

That evening when he returned home, his father asked him:

"Where is your bride, my son? And why do you still have the cattle with you?"

"I brought them home because the pretty maid had no teeth and I would never have married her," answered his son.

The father was much saddened, but his second-born son intervened and said:

"I fear that my brother exaggerates. Father, give me permission to go and see if this pretty maid really has no teeth as he says. I have to get married too, don't I?"

The father cheered up and gave his consent. The following morning, the second son left with the three cows and the two oxen, and when he reached the girl's village, he was welcomed with great ceremony. He explained the reason for his coming, and her father said:

"Daughter, here is your bridegroom, go home with him!"

The girl said nothing and followed the young man. But lo and behold, at the same point along the way as on the day before, she began to softly sing:

"Watch out, watch out, my handsome youth! I'm a pretty maid but I haven't a tooth!"

The young man immediately stopped and asked her to open her mouth because he wanted to check and see if what she was saying was true. The girl did not have to be persuaded; she opened her mouth and showed him the two black lines. Naturally the young man immediately brought her back, took back the cattle, and when he returned home and his father inquired about the bride, he answered:

"My brother was right—And I won't marry a toothless woman either! I gave her back to her father and took back the cattle."

The third son then came forward and asked his father's permission to go and have a look, too. His father consented, but the eldest brother took offense and asked him:

"What do you take us for? A pair of imbeciles? Do you think that we wouldn't have married her if she'd had her teeth?"

"Oh, that's not it, my brother!" replied the youngest. "The fact is that you have inspired me with a great desire to see what a toothless girl looks like, that's all!"

So the next day, the third son left with the three cows and the two oxen and went to the girl's village. Her father greeted him affectionately and said to him:

"You seem very young to be taking a wife. But seeing as both of your brothers gave her back to me, I will accept your cattle and you can take my daughter."

He called the girl and told her to go with the young man. The girl said neither yes nor no; she just set off with her new fiancé.

When they reached the same point along the way as on the two previous occasions, the young maid began to softly sing as usual:

"Watch out, watch out, my handsome youth! I'm a pretty maid but I haven't a tooth!"

"Open your mouth!" the young man said to her, with his heart in his throat. The girl obeyed and showed him the two black lines. He was astonished at the sight of them, but he acted as if nothing were wrong, and simply said, "It doesn't matter; let's go on."

They came to a river, and the young maid, after casting a glance at the young man, once again began to softly sing:

"Watch out, watch out, my handsome youth! I'm a pretty maid but I haven't a tooth!"

The young man didn't pay any attention to the song, and began to ford the river at its shallowest point. But when they reached the middle of the river, he held the girl tightly to his chest with one arm and ordered her to open her mouth nice and wide. The frightened bride-to-be obeyed, and with his free arm, the young man deftly rubbed her mouth with some sand that he had picked up from the riverbed.

The black lines melted away, and a beautiful set of teeth appeared. The two young people kissed happily and continued on to the village.

The two older brothers, seeing the girl arrive with the youngest of them all, ran to their father and said:

"Father, quick, come and see that nitwit youngest son of yours! He's given away the cattle, and brought that toothless thing home with him!"

In the meantime, after he arrived in the village, the young man had handed the young maid over to one of his sisters so that she could bring her to his mother in the women's house. Of course, all of the village girls, having heard about this curious maid, gathered around her and began to tell silly stories in order to make her laugh, and thus find out if what people were saying about her teeth was true. The girl held herself back for a little while, but then she laughed merrily, and all the village girls saw to their great amazement that she had a very beautiful set of teeth.

The youngest son went to his father and told him that he had agreed to take the young maid as his wife, and that the wedding would take place soon. His father was unable to hide his disappointment and said:

"All right, my son, but you have exchanged those fine cattle for a toothless girl and you know that we are not rich."

The lad burst out laughing and told his father what he had done to make his betrothed's beautiful set of teeth reappear.

So the father had himself brought to the girl and said to her:

"Please don't be offended, and do comply with my request: Open your mouth and I will give you this beautiful silver necklace."

The young maid gave a beautiful smile, and the father saw with his own eyes that the teeth were indeed there, and that they really were beautiful!

Then he called his older sons and said to them:

"Look, you fools! The girl does have teeth, but you weren't able to find them. Your younger brother deserves to have her as his wife; and remember, he is below you only in age!"

One Good Turn Deserves Another

☗ ASHANTI ☗

I t is told that there once lived an eagle who, like all eagles, liked to wander hither and yon, all over the vast sky that hangs above the Earth.

Now one day, the eagle saw an old woman limping down a narrow lane, and this aroused her curiosity. She flew down and saw that one of the old woman's legs was completely covered with sores, and that was why she was having trouble walking. So the eagle said to the old woman:

"You poor thing! How do you manage to stay on your feet with your leg in such awful condition?"

"Well," answered the old woman, "I force myself. I'm trying to go on just long enough to reach the marketplace in the village; I need to buy a little bit of milk and grain."

The eagle was touched, but knowing the ingratitude of humans, she was not sure what she should do. Then she said:

"If you humans weren't the way you are, I would help you! But if I do one of you a good turn today, I am certain that tomorrow you will repay me with an equal amount of harm!"

But the old woman said, "Not me! I would never do that!"

The eagle, who had a good heart, allowed herself to be convinced.

"If what you are saying is true," she said, "you deserve my help. Now close your eyes, count to ten, and open them again!"

The old woman closed her eyes, counted to ten, and opened them again.

Then the eagle said to her, "There, now look at your sore leg."

Somewhat nervously, the old woman bent down and looked at her leg—it was as good as new! There wasn't even a trace of the terrible sore that had been hurting her.

"But I want to do even more," the eagle went on, without giving the old woman time to thank her. "Even if your legs are working now, the village is too far away. Close your eyes, count to twenty, and open them again."

And the old woman closed her eyes, counted to twenty, and opened them again. And she saw that for miles and miles around, the forest had been changed into fertile fields.

"It would be good, however," continued the eagle, not paying any attention to the

old woman's astonishment, "if you received constant help and companionship. Close your eyes, count to thirty, and open them again."

The old woman closed her eyes once more, counted to thirty, and opened them again. All around her spread a large village, dense with huts and full of people. The men were going into the fields, the women were threshing grain in front of their houses, the cows were grazing, and the chickens were scratching.

"Old woman, all of this is yours!" said the eagle finally. "Go, and be happy!"

"Thank you, thank you!" the old woman managed to stammer. "What a generous soul you are! What can I do to repay you?"

"I don't want anything extraordinary," replied the eagle. "All I need is that leafy tree at the edge of the village, because it's time for me to build my nest and raise my little ones."

"If you truly don't want anything else, . . ." said the old woman, "what you ask is such a trifle; make that tree your home and live in peace!"

Then the eagle bowed, flew up into the tree, alighted, and built a fine, sturdy nest of branches and leaves. A little while passed, and she laid two eggs. She brooded the eggs for

the proper amount of time, and then two eaglets were born. And immediately mother eagle went off in search of food to bring to her little ones.

In the meantime, the old woman's granddaughter, who had joined her grandmother in the new village and who was very spoiled, began to whine morning, noon, and night.

"Boo-hoo-hoo," went the granddaughter.

"What's the matter with you, girl?" the old woman finally asked.

"I'm hungry," answered the granddaughter.

"Hungry? But you lack for nothing here!"

"But I'm hungry for something special. I feel like having a nice eaglet, that's what I'm hungry for!"

The old woman was astonished, and she tried to gain some time.

"Where am I going to find a baby eagle?" said the grandmother.

"Give me a nice eaglet to eat or I'll die!" insisted the wayward little girl.

At that, the grandmother became frightened, summoned the men of the village, and

asked them to cut down the leafy tree at the edge of the village in order to catch one of the eagle's children.

The men seized their axes and began to strike great blows on the tree trunk. The bigger of the two eaglets jumped up on the edge of the nest and called to his mama for help.

He sounded something like this:

"Sango, oh Sango! Oh Sango, Sango!"

From afar the mother, who was flying in search of food, heard her son's cry and was back in a flash. She flew over the tree, which was just about to fall, and shrieked:

"Sanguri!"

At once the tree straightened up, and its wound closed, while an abyss opened up beneath the men's feet and they fell into it. Then the earth covered them up.

The eagle gave the food to her children, calmed them down, and said to them:

"Now I must go back to the hunt. These men were crazy, but the old woman who rules the village is my friend. Whatever she may choose to do, don't worry. You have nothing to fear from her." And she flew away.

Meanwhile, the granddaughter had started to whine and throw tantrums again—so loudly that the old woman couldn't stand it any longer. She summoned some other men and asked them to bring her the eagle's young.

So they went off with their axes and began to chop down the tree. Once again, the bigger of the two eaglets jumped up on the edge of the nest and cried:

"Sango, oh Sango! Oh Sango, Sango!"

He called and called his mother, but this time she did not hear him. The tree fell to the ground, and the men carried away the two eaglets. The first one they handed over to the old woman, but the second, the bigger one, managed to escape and perch on the roof of a large hut. While the people of the village tried to catch him, the old woman roasted the one they had captured and gave it to her granddaughter to eat.

And then, a little while later, the eagle came back. She saw the fallen tree, the ruined nest, and she flew to the village. She found one of her children on the roof of a hut surrounded by howling men, and she asked him what had happened. As soon as she heard what had occurred, she took her son and brought him to safety on the mountain (which from that day forward became the home of the eagles). Then she went back down to the village and went to see the old woman.

"Old woman," she said bitterly, "you're really a fine one!" She drew herself up and exclaimed: *"Sanguri!"*—and all of the people vanished into the air. Again she said: *"Sanguri!"*—and all of the huts fell to the ground. And again: *"Sanguri!"*—and what was once a village became a forest again. *"Sanguri!"*—and once again the old woman had a leg covered with sores. Then with all the scorn that an eagle is capable of expressing, she added: "Old woman, this is all you deserve!"—and she vanished forever atop the mountain.

The lesson of this story is: "Do unto others as you would have others do unto you."

The Dog, the Cat, the Pigeon, and the Magic Ring

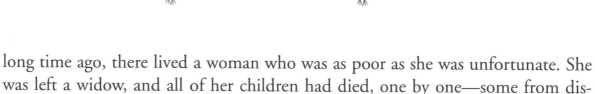

ASHANTI

A long time ago, there lived a woman who was as poor as she was unfortunate. She was left a widow, and all of her children had died, one by one—some from disease, some in accidents, and others in war. Only her youngest son was left. He was the sole consolation of her unfortunate life, and he really had an excellent disposition and a generous heart.

One day her son, who had awakened earlier than usual, went to his mother and said to her:

"Mother, give me a bit of gold dust; I want to go and buy some salt in Village-on-the-seashore."

The mother, who had a great deal of faith in her boy, said:

"How much do you need?"

"Give me a pinch of it," replied the boy.

His mother gave him the gold dust, and after gathering into a bundle what he would need for the trip, he set off.

Along the way, he ran into a man who was taking his black-and-white spotted dog to the market to sell.

"I would like to buy him!" said the boy, who had always longed for a dog's loving companionship.

"Why, you're not much more than a little boy. How are you going to pay for him?" said the man.

"Don't worry about it. How much does he cost?"

"Well, let's make it a pinch of gold dust."

"Ha! Here's your pinch of gold dust." And the boy handed over the gold dust, took the dog, and went back home.

When his mother saw that he was back already and, what's more, with a dog, she was quite taken aback:

"Why on earth didn't you get the salt in Village-on-the-seashore?"

"Because I bought this pretty dog with the gold dust."

The mother said, "Oh!"

And after a little while she didn't think about it anymore. But barely a month had gone by when the boy once more said to his mother:

"Mother, give me a little more gold dust; I would like to go to the marketplace to see if I can strike some kind of a good deal."

"My son, I fear that you will waste it like the last time. . . ."

"Don't worry! You'll see that you will have nothing to complain about."

Because she loved this last child of hers too much, the mother gave in and handed him the gold dust.

The boy set off on the road to the marketplace, and after a while, he saw a man holding a cat in his arms. And no mistake about it, it really was a pretty cat! And the boy couldn't keep himself from saying:

"I would like to buy your cat. I like the agility of a cat; it's the only animal that always lands on its feet."

"I can't sell it to you," answered the cat's owner. "I just now bought it so that it can chase the mice that are dancing around in my bedroom. And then, how might you pay me for it?"

"Because I am just a boy? Don't worry! How much do you want?"

"If you really insist. . . . Give me two pinches of gold dust."

The boy paid him and took the cat.

He went back home again, and his mother was quite surprised to see him back already.

"Mother, look at this pretty little cat! I couldn't resist temptation and I bought it."

His mother gazed at him sadly and exclaimed:

"Oh my son, I thought that you were very different!" And she scolded him and complained, but in the end she had to resign herself to the situation.

Some forty days passed, and the boy said:

"Mother, give me some more gold dust. I want to set myself up in business, and this time I won't disappoint you."

"My poor son, all we have left are these three pinches . . . take them anyway; do with them what you wish, but remember, after these, there are no more."

"Have faith!" said the boy, and at dawn the following day, he took up his pack and set off.

He had been on the road for a short time when, along the way, he met a hunter, carrying a pigeon. The boy realized that the hunter was bringing it home to cook it up for himself, so he said:

"I would like to buy your pigeon; I like pigeons when they make that strange murmuring sound of theirs."

"I don't feel like selling it!" responded the hunter.

"But I can pay you well for it!"

"Oh really? If I had to sell it, I would ask at least three pinches of gold dust."

"Well, here are your three pinches!" The boy took the pigeon and went back home again.

As one can easily imagine, as soon as his mother saw him at the door with a pigeon on his shoulder, she was seized with despair.

"Oh my son, what have you done? Now we don't have anything anymore!"

The boy didn't know what to say to her. Feeling sorry for what he had done, he sat down outside the door of the house with the dog at his feet, the cat in his lap, and the pigeon on his shoulder.

"And now what?" he thought. "What should I do to make amends for my thoughtlessness? How can I repay my mother for her sacrifice?" And while he was feeling guilty in this manner, he heard a voice very close to his ear saying:

"Calm down, I will help you!"

To his great astonishment, the boy realized that it was the pigeon who was talking.

"So it really is true that animals can speak if we know how to listen to them!" he said.

The pigeon didn't pay much attention to the impression he had made on his master, and he went on:

"My dear fellow, you need to know that in my village I was a very important chief; I was just about to fly away on a nice little trip when that hunter who caught me showed up. And if it weren't for your buying me, at this moment I would be dead and broiled. So take me back to my village, and all of my people will demonstrate their immeasurable gratitude."

The boy was somewhat perplexed and said:

"And what if you're telling me a fib so you can run away?"

"If you don't trust me, tie a rope to my foot and then I'll be forced to stay close to you."

The boy took a long rope, tied it to the pigeon's foot, and following the bird's directions, he slowly walked to the village.

When they reached the first houses, two children playing with colored marbles sprang to their feet and began to run as soon as they saw the bird, crying:

"The chief! The chief has come back!"

Then everyone, men and women both, ran up to meet the two travelers, uttering cries of joy and bearing the royal banners as is customary when receiving a king.

Then they all made merry. The pigeon king told all that had happened to him, and when he said that the boy had given the last of his gold to save him from certain death, great was the gratitude of old and young alike. First the Queen Mother, then all of the elders in turn presented the boy with a jugful of gold dust. Finally the witch doctor slipped a ring off his finger and gave it to the boy, saying:

"Take this ring, and whatever wish you may express, this magic ring will grant it."

The boy remained as a guest of the village for three days and three nights, but at last the time came for him to leave. He said an emotional farewell to the pigeon, filled a large goatskin with gold dust, and went home to his mother.

He found her on the threshing floor where she was feeding the hens. He ran to her and hugged her. Then he showed her the gold dust and the ring, and hastened to tell her everything so that the poor woman wouldn't faint from astonishment.

"Now," concluded the boy, "I will go into the forest, and with the help of this ring, I will build a new village for us to live in."

He went out of the house, and headed into the depths of the forest at a good pace. After walking a long way, he came to a spot where the forest was so dense with trees and bushes that it was not possible to go any farther. So he placed the magic jewel on the ground and commanded:

"Ring, make a free and open space out of this area full of trees and brambles!"

Immediately the trees fell, uprooted, to the ground, crushing the bushes.

Then the boy commanded, "Ring, stack up all of these branches and burn them until nothing but ashes remain!"

In the twinkling of an eye, all of the twigs and branches from the trees piled themselves up in the middle of the clearing, and who knows how, caught fire and were turned to ashes in an instant.

Again the boy ordered:

"Ring, make houses—a lot of houses—rise up in this clearing!"

At once, big and small houses sprouted from the ground like mushrooms.

Finally he ordered:

"Ring, do not let these houses remain empty, but make people live in them!"

Like magic, men and women appeared, going in and out of their houses, walking, talking—all going about their business as if they had been there forever.

Happy with all that he had done, the boy went to get his mother and appointed her queen of the village. And he proclaimed himself the leader of the new community.

Now, you should know that about one day's walk from the newly risen village, there

lived Ananse the spider, who one day heard of this happy town that had miraculously appeared in the middle of the forest. Ananse became so curious about it that he decided to go and have a look in person, and so he set off to call on the boy.

"Congratulations, my sincerest congratulations!" said the spider, looking around. "Fortune has finally smiled on you, eh? I remember that you were poor and thin the last time I saw you . . . but how did you do all this?"

The boy, whose frank nature had not changed, told him everything. The spider Ananse then felt within himself a great envy and a strong desire to get hold of the ring. But on the outside, he acted as if nothing were wrong. He cordially said his good-byes, and went back to his own village. As soon as he arrived, he summoned his nephew and said to him:

"Do me a favor and go to that new village; ask for the young chief, and offer him this fine gourd full of wine as a gift. Make friends with him, and as soon as you can, steal the ring from him."

The nephew, who was quite worthy of such an uncle, didn't stick around to discuss the matter, but went to the new village, bearing the wine for the boy-chief. The two quickly made friends, and Ananse's nephew was invited to stay for as long as he wished as a guest of the community.

So three days went by, and at dawn of the fourth day, the boy-chief wanted to go have a swim in the river. He slipped the ring off and placed it on the table. When Ananse's nephew was all alone, he stole the ring and ran away at full speed to his uncle's village.

Ananse had barely taken possession of the magic ring when he commanded that a village arise that would be even bigger and more beautiful than the young chief's. And in a flash, his wish was granted.

Meanwhile, the boy had returned from the river and had searched in vain for both the ring and his guest. Worried, he called upon the spirit of the woods for advice.

"You have been too trusting, and as a result, unwise!" the spirit said to him. "Ananse sent his nephew to you so he could steal your ring, and now that he has it, he has had a village built, twice the size of yours and more beautiful."

"So I have been taken in . . . but tell me, how can I get the ring back?" asked the boy.

"Send your dog, Ocraman, and your cat, Ocra, to Ananse's home. Only they can accomplish this deed."

The boy went back home and summoned the dog and cat so he could explain the job to them.

However, in the meantime Ananse the spider had also gone to a spirit who had warned him of the two envoys' intentions.

And so he laid his plan. He mixed some good, finely minced meat with a special potion that would put anyone who tasted it to sleep, and he scattered the meat along the road.

Then he began to wait.

Ocraman and Ocra, side by side, were already on their way and had reached a fork in the road. They sniffed this way and they sniffed that way, and they quickly picked up the smell of the meat that had been abundantly scattered along the path to the left.

"There's something funny going on here," said the cat. "I don't like it. Let's turn to the right!"

But the dog, who couldn't resist the smell of the meat, didn't pay any attention to the cat and took the left-hand path. He found the meat, and he gulped it down in no time and immediately fell asleep.

But the cat had turned in the right direction, and after a little while he reached Ananse's village. He found the house and went in; the spider was sleeping, stretched out on a carpet of leaves.

The cat stealthily searched all over the place, and then . . . *Eureka!* He found the ring inside a strongbox. But at that precise instant, Ananse showed signs of waking up, so the cat was forced to hide. Just then an unwary little mouse passed close to him, and in a second, he had him in his paws.

"Don't eat me!" whispered the little mouse.

"I wouldn't dream of it," replied the cat, "as long as you would be willing to help me. . . ."

"Help? Certainly! What do I have to do?"

"Do you see that strongbox over there? Ananse the spider keeps a ring in it that he stole from my master. Go get it and bring it to me without making a sound and your life will be spared."

The mouse didn't have to be told twice. He noiselessly slipped over to the strongbox, and he very quietly started to gnaw away at the cover with his sharp little teeth. Once he had made a hole in the cover, he let himself down into the box, slipped the ring onto his tail, and went back to the cat. Ocra thanked the little mouse and kept his promise. Then he ran away with the magic jewel. And soon he reached the spot where he had left the dog.

"So, you're sleeping?" said Ocra. "And where has all that meat that was here gone?"

"What do you mean sleeping?!" replied Ocraman. "I didn't feel good at all. And as for meat, there wasn't even a trace of it; we were mistaken."

The cat realized that Ocraman was lying to save face, but he acted as if he didn't notice.

Then the dog asked him about the ring.

"Well done!" he said after Ocra had told him everything. "But now we have to cross the river at its deepest part. You, like all cats, hate the water, and will be forced to jump, and the ring might get away from you when you're jumping. It might be better if you gave it to me, since I know how to swim. I'll hold it in my mouth, and it will be safe."

The cat had to admit that the dog was right, and he gave him the ring. When they reached the riverbank, the dog plunged into the water and began to swim with vigor. But the cat made a leap onto a big tree trunk that was being carried on the current, and from there . . . *Hop!*

With another leap, he came back down on dry land on the other bank. While he was still in the middle of the river, the dog all of a sudden felt tired from the effort. He wanted to catch his breath, so he opened his mouth a little, and the ring slipped from his teeth and disappeared into the depths.

"Where is the ring?" Ocra asked him as soon as the dog reached the shore.

"Well . . . you see . . ." said Ocraman, very ill at ease, "it fell out of my mouth in the middle of the river!"

At first the cat got angry. Then he gave way to despair. But all of a sudden, a big fish leapt out of the water near the shore. Ocra immediately seized him, and holding the fish by the tail, the cat said to him:

"You wouldn't by any chance have seen a certain ring . . ." and he squeezed the paw

that held the fish even more tightly. The fish's only answer was to open his mouth wide, and the ring tumbled out. Ocra took the ring and threw the fish back into the water.

Then the dog begged the cat:

"Ocra, please, don't tell our master what happened!"

But the cat didn't answer because he was too angry at the dog. So when they got back home, the dog, for fear that the cat would reveal how things had gone, blamed Ocra for the troubles that he himself had caused.

But the boy had learned the truth from the spirit of the woods, and he wouldn't listen to the dog's excuses; he condemned the dog to sleep outdoors, and rewarded the cat, letting him stay indoors with him where it was warm.

The Spanking-Switch

 ASHANTI

Ananse the spider lived with his wife, Aso, and their three children, Skinny-Legs, Full-Belly, and Big-Head, in a house near the woods. Everyday like a good family man, Ananse went out to look for food.

One fine morning as he wandered hither and yon in search of a bite to eat, he found a very shiny, very clean dish beside a bush. And he exclaimed:

"What a beautiful dish!"

But to his great surprise, the dish replied, somewhat offended:

"My name is not 'Beautiful!' "

"And what might it be then?" said the spider whose curiosity had been aroused.

"My name is 'Fill-Up-and-Eat,' " said the dish.

So the spider said:

"Well then fill up and let's see!"

Immediately the bowl was filled with steaming hot soup.

Ananse didn't waste any time and ate it all up. When he was full, he rubbed his swollen belly and addressed the dish:

"You are a magic object, and as with everything that has to do with magic, there is something that undoes your powers. Tell me what it is."

"It's true," said the dish. "I am afraid of a gun wad and of a little gourd cup."

"Good!" said the spider, and he took the dish away with him.

When he got back home, he went up into the attic without anybody seeing him and hid the dish there. Then ever so quietly, he went back to the woods, got himself some food and brought it to his family. His wife, Aso, cooked it and called everyone in to supper.

Then the spider said:

"No wife, you need to eat more than I do. Please take my share and divide it up among you. If you are full, then I will be, too."

Aso was more than a little amazed, because her husband had always had a good appetite, but in order not to offend him, she divided his share among the children, and they ate their meal.

In the meantime, Ananse had made up some excuse and quickly gone up to the attic by way of the outside staircase. He sat down beside the dish and said:

"This dish really is beautiful!"

And the dish said:

"I've already told you that my name is not 'Beautiful!'"

"Oh, that's right!" said the spider. "What is your name again? I've forgotten it. . . ."

"My name is 'Fill-Up-and-Eat.'"

"Then fill up and let's see," said Ananse. And immediately the dish was filled to the brim with tender, steaming hot stew. The spider didn't waste time thinking, he just ate it all up.

So every day, for days and days, Ananse secretly went up into the attic. Every day he pretended not to remember the dish's name, put the dish to the test, and his meal was assured.

But the eldest of the children, Skinny-Legs, noticed that even though his father never ate, he hadn't lost an ounce. On the contrary, for some time he seemed even more rotund than usual. So he suspected that his father had come up with some kind of a scheme, and he decided to keep an eye on his movements. After some time he noticed that when

Ananse thought that they were all asleep, he stealthily went up into the attic. So one day, he waited until his father had gone into the woods to get food, and then he climbed up the stairs.

He looked here, and he looked there, and then he finally saw the dish. He called his mother and brothers, and they all began to talk.

"What do you think of this?" said Skinny-Legs. "Isn't this dish beautiful?"

"My name is not 'Beautiful!' " said the dish, to their general astonishment.

"And what, if you please, is your name?" said Full-Belly.

"My name is 'Fill-Up-and-Eat.' "

So Big-Head said, "Well then, fill up and let's see!"

At once the dish was filled to the brim with peanut and heart of palm soup.

"This dish is bewitched!" thought the mother, and with a gesture, she restrained the children who were already about to eat the soup. Then she said, "Of course, since you are magical, you must be subject to some kind of a counterspell. Tell me what it is please, so that we can avoid hurting you by accident."

"It's true," replied the dish. "I am afraid of a gun wad and of a little gourd cup."

Then Aso said, "So my children, your father likes to play the generous soul! Well now we're going to teach him a lesson!" And she ordered her children to go and get the wad and the cup for her.

Skinny-Legs, quite satisfied with himself, went down into the kitchen, got the two objects, and went back up to the attic, whistling. Then the mother took the gun wad and touched the dish, and it went "Ouch!" Next she took the little gourd cup and touched the dish again, and again it went "Ouch!" Then one by one, they all went back downstairs and began to wait for Ananse.

Not long afterward, there he was, back from the woods with supper.

"Please, eat my share, too," he said as he did every evening as soon as his wife called him to the table. "You need it more than I do. If you are full, then I will be, too."

The mother and children ate, and then went off to bed. Ever so quietly, the spider went up into the attic and took the dish in his hand.

"Oh yes! This dish really is beautiful!" he exclaimed as usual, but he got no response.

"I said," he insisted, "this dish is beautiful!"—Silence.—"It is a beautiful dish!"—Nothing.—"Beautiful dish!"—Dead silence.—"Beautiful, I said!" But the dish wasn't responding any more. Then Ananse began to look around the room, and he discovered the gun wad and the little gourd cup in a corner.

"Aso and the children have found out everything!" Ananse despaired. But instead of realizing that he was at least as much to blame as his family, who had simply done wrong out of curiosity, he came down from the attic and went into the woods, plotting revenge.

After walking a long way, he felt tired and stopped under a big tree. He lay down, and continuing to mutter threatening plans, he closed his eyes and fell asleep. He dreamed that a bird was speaking to him from high up in the tree, and was advising him how to punish his untrustworthy family. In the dream, the bird said:

"Ananse, move those leaves next to you, and there you will find a nice and clean, very smooth little switch. Take it."

And in his dream, the spider moved the leaves and found the stick that the bird had told him about.

"Now," continued the bird, "pay a nice compliment to the switch."

And Ananse said:

"Beautiful little switch of mine!"

"My name is not 'Beautiful Little Switch of Mine!' " she replied resentfully.

"Well then tell me your name!" said the spider.

"My name is 'Spanking-Switch.' "

"If that's so, then spank a bit and let's see!" replied Ananse.

The switch didn't need to be persuaded, and began whipping left and right! The poor spider didn't know where to turn anymore, and he jumped back and forth trying to escape those extremely painful cuts. "Ouch! Ouch! Ooouuch!" shrieked the poor fellow, but the switch didn't stop striking him for a second.

"Oh poor me!" groaned Ananse. "Isn't there any way to stop it?"

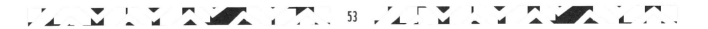

"Fool that you are!" the bird screamed at him from high up in the tree. "It's just what you deserve. But for now, maybe that's enough. Say 'Be careful!' and the switch will stop."

And the spider yelled:

"Be careful! Be careful!" and immediately the switch stopped its whipping.

Then Ananse thought that he had found the way to avenge himself. He took 'Spanking-Switch' with him and went back home.

As soon as he arrived, he gave the food for supper to his wife, and told her to cook it and divide it up between the children because he didn't need any of it. And he concluded as usual, "If you are full, then I will be, too," and disappeared into the attic with the switch, taking care, this time, that his wife and children noticed.

Once in the attic, he put the switch in a corner and went out onto the outside staircase. He left the door ajar and waited. An hour passed, and then, there was his son Skinny-Legs who immediately began to search. After finding the switch, he ran to summon his mother and brothers.

"What do you think of this?" asked Skinny-Legs. "Isn't this a beautiful switch?"

"My name is not 'Beautiful Switch!' " she exclaimed.

"And what is your name?" asked Full-Belly.

"My name is 'Spanking-Switch.' "

"Well, spank a bit and let's see!" concluded Big-Head.

Oh that he had never said that! At once the switch began to lash about right and left, and a chorus of "Ouch! Ouch! Ooouuuch!" rang out everywhere.

"It serves you right!" thought Ananse, hiding behind the door. Then he decided that they had had enough, and he said, "Be careful!"

The switch stopped and Ananse woke up from his dream!

The Spirit of the River

✦ KIKUYU ✦

Ghiase was the most renowned warrior of his tribe, and so it was natural that he would wish to have a wife who was worthy of him. And one day, after a long search, and after having rejected dozens of possible maids, he found a girl who was without a doubt the most beautiful in the whole area. Her name was Emme, and she lived on the other side of the river. Ghiase didn't want to waste any time, and he begged the girl's parents to allow him to wed their daughter immediately. They had no objections, and Ghiase, satisfied, went back to his village to organize the wedding feast.

Emme's father was one of the richest and most powerful men of his tribe, and since he wanted his daughter to make her entrance into her husband's village suitably escorted, he presented her with the most beautiful of his slave girls and ordered his youngest daughter to accompany her sister.

So the three girls set off. They would have to walk for the whole day, but their excitement over the wedding would succeed in overcoming their tiredness.

It was already the hour when the sun is low on the horizon and the first star appears in the sky, when the girls arrived at the river in sight of Ghiase's village. To refresh themselves a bit and make themselves more presentable, the girls decided to take a bath.

Now, in those waters there lived a spirit, the absolute lord of the river from its source to its mouth. But Emme, who didn't know this, confidently plunged in while her sister and the slave girl took their time getting undressed.

If Emme and her sister were unaware of the spirit's presence, the slave girl, whose submissive and polite exterior concealed a wicked heart, was very much aware of it, and she deliberately did not hold her mistress back. On the contrary, standing on the bank, she shouted to her mistress to push out into the middle of the river where the water was clearer. And suddenly, two enormous pale blue arms emerged from the water and seized the poor girl who, in an instant, disappeared into the depths of the river.

Her little sister gave way to despair, but the slave girl threatened her, and showed herself for what she was:

"Stop your crying or I'll throw you in the river and the spirit will get you, too! From now on, *you* will be *my* slave, and beware if you tell anybody what happened!"

And so she forced the little sister to load their baggage on her back, and together they set off for Ghiase's village on the other bank of the river.

When Ghiase saw the slave with the little girl following behind, he was unable to restrain a gesture of surprise. He didn't think she looked like the girl he had asked to marry, but he attributed the change to weariness from the trip and to the darkness of the night. So he showed the two girls into the house and treated them like honored guests.

The next day Ghiase introduced his betrothed to the assembled tribe, and they were all quite puzzled; they grumbled among themselves:

"Didn't Ghiase describe her as a matchless beauty? This girl is rather ordinary!"

But they didn't say anything to Ghiase because they were all fond of him and didn't want to hurt his feelings.

The days passed by, and Ghiase, who was inwardly more and more hesitant, put off the wedding ceremony for as long as possible with one excuse one day and another excuse the next.

The slave girl began to get irritated, and she took her anger out on Emme's little sister. She missed no opportunity to scold her and mistreat her, often going as far as beating her with a stick. Even worse, in order to torment her with the memory of her sister's

tragic end, every morning she ordered the little girl to go to the river to fetch water in huge jugs.

The poor little thing, for fear of suffering the same fate as Emme, held her tongue and didn't attempt to rebel.

Ghiase, who had become aware of the bullying endured by the little one, had reproached his supposed fiancée, who from that time on pretended to be as sweet as the fruit of the palm tree, in his presence. As soon as Ghiase left, she became even more evil than before: threats, malice, and . . . blows!

One day, the little girl went to the river as usual to fetch water, but when she tried to lift the jug and place it on her head, she just couldn't do it. It was too big and too heavy, just like her misfortunes. Then her eyes filled with tears, and she sat down on the river-bank and began to sob.

Suddenly the surface of the river became agitated, and a very beautiful young woman sprang out of the water. It was Emme, who now lived as a prisoner in the spirit's watery palace. Hearing her little sister crying, she had implored her jailer to let her surface for a little while, just long enough to comfort her sister. The spirit had agreed, sure of the power he had over her.

When the little girl saw Emme again, she felt as if she were going to faint, but her sister's gentle words convinced her that she was not dreaming. Then she fell into her sister's arms and told her how she was being treated by the slave girl and how alone and hopeless she felt.

"And my future husband?" Emme asked her at last.

"Every day he postpones the wedding date," replied her sister.

"I'm convinced that everything will work out for the best, you'll see," Emme consoled her. "But I have to go back now, otherwise the spirit of the river will not let me see you the next time you come. You will come back, won't you?"

"Oh certainly, dear sister! Every morning!"

"Until tomorrow then, and be brave!" And with that, she dove back down.

A few days passed in this way: The little girl would go to the river to get water, and her sister would come up on the bank to talk to her. They'd stay together for a little while, comforting each other by turns, and then they each would go their own way.

One morning while the little girl was bending over the stretch of water and calling her sister, a hunter from Ghiase's tribe passed by. Hearing the cry "Emme! Emme!" the hunter hid behind a dense thicket of bushes and watched what was going on. After a little while, the waters of the river burst open. To his great astonishment, he saw a very beautiful girl climb up onto the bank, affectionately embrace the little girl, and then begin talking to her.

When the lovely creature plunged back into the river, and the little girl left with her cargo of water, the hunter cut through the forest at a good pace, heading toward the village. There he found Ghiase busy making himself a spear.

"Brave Ghiase," he said excitedly, "a little while ago I saw your bride's slave girl on the riverbank."

"Yes, she goes there every morning to fetch water," said Ghiase.

"But listen to this!" replied the hunter. "I heard her calling out and invoking the name Emme."

"Emme?" interrupted Ghiase, baffled.

"Exactly, and a very beautiful girl came up out of the river and began to talk to her."

"But Emme is the name. . . ." Ghiase went on completely confused.

"I know it's the name of the girl you chose for your wife. Listen, Ghiase, in my opinion, the spirit of the river managed to kidnap your real fiancée and he's holding her prisoner, while the one who showed up in the village is an impostor!"

"That has to be it!" said Ghiase thoughtfully. "In fact, the more I look at her, the less I recognize her. Tomorrow morning we'll go to the river together and find out if our suspicions are well-founded. Thank you, my friend!"

So on the following morning, Ghiase and the hunter hid behind the bushes near the river and began to wait. The little girl arrived and began to call her sister's name, and after a few minutes, there was Emme, coming out of the water in all her beauty. Immediately recognizing his real bride, Ghiase could barely restrain a cry of joy.

When Emme dove back into the water, the two men went back to the village, discussing how to free the young woman from the spirit's power.

"I think," said the hunter, "that we will never manage it by ourselves. Only the old woman of the river can help you."

"Of course!" cried Ghiase, full of enthusiasm. "She's my only hope!"

Nobody knew *how* old the old woman of the river was: Some said a hundred, some two hundred, some a thousand. There were even those who maintained that she had always existed. But everybody knew her old hut on the left bank of the river, which was respected even by the fearsome hyenas who never showed themselves in those parts.

Ghiase went to see the old woman and related the matter to her. And the old woman said to him:

"There *is* something that can be done. Get yourself a white goat, a white hen, a white cloak, and a basket of eggs. When you have found all these things, bring them to me, and we shall see."

Ghiase left and came back with what he had been asked for. The old woman said that they had to wait for the new moon and that he could go back to the village; she would take care of everything.

The new moon arrived, and the old woman went by herself to the other side of the river. First she pushed the goat into the water, and then the hen. She threw the eggs in one

by one, and finally she spread the white cloak on the surface of the river and it glided away on the gentle waves.

At once the waters parted and Emme came out, walking up to the bank on the cloak.

"I bid you welcome, Emme!" exclaimed the old woman. "Do not be afraid, I have come on Ghiase's behalf. Trust me."

She led the girl to her hut, and sent for her betrothed who arrived in a flash along with the hunter. And so finally the two lovers were able to embrace each other again. A little while later, the little girl was also secretly informed of the situation and was led to the old woman's hut. Anyone who might have chanced to pass by at that moment would not have been able to tell if they were having a party or mourning a death, so great was the overlapping of laughter and sobbing in that hut. Then they agreed upon a plan, and the little girl was sent back to the village to spring the trap.

As soon as she entered the house, she immediately began to berate the slave girl:

"You wicked creature! So, you wanted to marry Ghiase, huh? You killed my sister so you could steal her fiancé!"

"Shut up, you fool!" screamed the impostor in a towering rage. "I'll fix you now!"

She grabbed the stick and began to chase the little girl, who swiftly slipped through the door and took off at a run for the old woman's hut. There, Emme and the others were waiting for her.

The little girl took refuge inside, and when the slave girl reached the threshold, there was Emme. The treacherous impostor didn't understand anything anymore. Filled with terror at the sight of that ghost, she turned around and began to run in the opposite direction. But without realizing it, she suddenly found herself on the riverbank. Pushed on by her momentum, she fell headlong into the water. Immediately the spirit's blue arms rose up out of the depths, grabbed her, and dragged her down to his palace.

The slave girl was a prisoner of the spirit of the river. And a few days later, Emme and Ghiase were finally able to happily get married.

The Golden Child and the Silver Child

Powerful Nyame, the most illustrious of the heavenly gods, lived in a magnificent palace surrounded by beautiful cultivated fields, way up high, on a cushion of pink clouds. He lived happily and lacked for nothing, but one day he realized that he was bored. How was this possible? He was alone too much, and therefore he decided to take a wife.

So he summoned the four most beautiful and refined maidens in the whole tribe to the palace, showed them in, offered them something to eat and drink, and finally asked each of them:

"Tell me, if you became my wife, what would you do for me?"

The first, Coco by name, replied, "I would keep the halls of the palace tidy, and I would oversee the slave girls."

And the second one said, "Every day I would make exquisite little snacks for you with my own hands."

And then the third one said, "I would spin and weave all the cotton from your fields for you."

And finally the fourth said, "I would give you special children."

At these words, Nyame had no more doubts, and he declared that the last girl would become his wife. The first girl, Coco, was very disappointed at having been rejected, and she felt choked with envy and jealousy; nonetheless, she cleverly hid her true feelings and succeeded in making people think that she was the bride's friend. She even became her lady-in-waiting.

The young couple loved each other very much, and spent happy days together. Then one day, Nyame had to be away from home to visit some lands that had been stricken by famine.

And while he was away on his journey, his wife gave birth to a pair of splendid twins: one completely made of gold, and the other of silver. She had said "special children," and she had kept her word.

The wicked Coco could not stand her rival's new joy. As soon as she had the chance, she took the two babies out of their cradle and placed them in a basket with a heavy lid. She went and hid the basket in the cavity of an old tree in the depths of the forest. Then she went back to the palace and placed two dreadful toads in the cradle.

As soon as Nyame returned home, the false friend welcomed him, saying:

"Congratulations, Nyame, you have become a father! Come and see your sons!"

And Nyame, brimming with happiness, ran into his wife's room where they kept the cradle. What horror he felt at the sight of the two toads! At first he was confused. But then confusion changed to sorrow, and then to rage, and finally to disgust. He gave orders to kill the two horrible little monsters, and turned his wife out of the palace.

Now, a hunter chanced to be chasing some game near the old hollow tree where the basket with Nyame's children was hidden. The hunter noticed the basket and grew curious. Forgetting about his quarry, he went over to the basket and opened it.

"What wonder is this?" he exclaimed when he saw the glittering gold and silver of the babies' skin.

"Do not be amazed," replied the newborns. "We are the sons of powerful Nyame."

Even though he was very poor, the man did not hesitate; he brought the babies home to his wife, and the new parents brought them up with love as if they had been their own children.

The years passed, and the two babies became fine young lads—kind, intelligent, and loving; nor had they neglected to reward the hunter's generosity insofar as they were able. Once a week, they rubbed their arms as hard as they could until gold and silver dust fell off. They gave the precious dust to their adoptive father so he could buy all that the family needed in the marketplace.

But one day the wife called her husband aside and said to him:

"Husband, I believe the time has come to part with these boys. I say this with a very heavy heart, but you know whose children they are, and it is right that they go back to their real father. We cannot keep them with us any longer—they are the descendants of powerful Nyame."

The hunter fumbled for some excuse, but then, realizing that his wife was right, he took each boy by the hand and took them back to Nyame.

But when they arrived at the palace, the hunter did not have the heart to provide the powerful god with too many explanations. So after bidding the boys good-bye, he left them in front of the gate after reminding them to behave themselves.

A little while later, Nyame came out and saw the two splendid children.

"Good heavens!" he exclaimed. "What miracle might this be?"

"No miracle," they said. "We are the sons of powerful Nyame." And without giving their father time to recover from his surprise, they began to sing their story in the sweet-

est of voices: The promise of respect and loyalty made to their mama, Coco's wicked deed, and the kindness of the hunter and his wife.

As he listened to them, Nyame's heart filled with joy. He welcomed his sons into the palace, and freed his wife from the hut where she had been held prisoner. Finally, he ordered Coco to go into the courtyard, and when she was right in the middle of it, he changed her into a hen. (Yet it seemed that she wasn't even very likable in that guise, since the other hens immediately began to peck at her!) Nyame then went to the hunter's hut and gave him some rich farmland as a way of thanks.

It is said that even today when Nyame's precious sons go for a swim in the great river in the heavens, the water that falls to the earth in the form of rain contains some gold and some silver dust, and whoever picks it up becomes rich.

How to Pay Off a Debt

EFIK-IBIBIO

Once upon a time, there was a hunter named Effiong who lived all alone in the forest. He was such a good hunter that he became very rich and was renowned throughout the area. He had only one dear friend, named Okun, who lived on the other side of the forest.

However, Effiong did have one serious fault: All that he earned—and he earned a lot—he wasted on expensive food and drink; he bought whatever appealed to him. Spending and spending without ever putting anything aside, he finally found himself in poverty. And not only that, but his success as a hunter seemed to be on the decline, because he couldn't manage to catch anything anymore, not even small game.

Day after day, Effiong grew poorer and poorer until he didn't even have the means to eat. So, swallowing his pride, he crossed the forest to go and see his friend, Okun.

"Okun," he said, "I have been reduced to poverty and I just don't know how to go on. You're my friend, Okun, can you make me a loan?"

"With pleasure," replied Okun. "Take these two hundred coins; pay me back when you can."

"Thank you so much for your generosity," Effiong replied to his friend. "Come and see me in a week. I will pay off my debt, and we will go hunting together."

Okun accepted the invitation, and the two friends said good-bye.

Some time before this, Effiong had made friends with a leopard and a cat that he had spared during a hunt. More recently, he had entered into a friendly relationship with a rooster and a goat on a farm where he had taken shelter during a violent thunderstorm.

The next morning, Effiong went to see the leopard and also asked him for a loan of two hundred coins.

"Come and get them back in a week," said the hunter when he had the coins in his pocket. "And if you don't find me at home, make yourself comfortable: Go on in and eat whatever is there."

Then Effiong went to see the goat, and asked for, and got, two hundred coins from her, too. He made her the same deal, and went away richer than when he had arrived.

The wildcat and the rooster were also honored with a visit, and were given the same exact promise:

"Come to my house in a week. And if I'm not there, make yourself comfortable!"

The week passed, and the day arrived when the hunter had to settle his accounts. Effiong got up while it was still dark, scattered a few handfuls of grain on the floor, and then left the house.

The sun began to come up, and the rooster crowed. After he crowed, he remembered the debt he was owed and he went to the hunter's house. He went in, but the house was empty. He thought about coming back later, but then he decided to wait for Effiong to return. As he was wandering around the house, he saw the grain on the floor, and remembering Effiong's invitation, he began to peck.

A little while later the wildcat also arrived. He went in and saw that there was nobody

there. But he remembered what Effiong had said to him, so he looked around for some food—just enough for a little snack. When he saw the rooster, he stalked him ever so quietly, was on him in a flash, and gulped him down in one mouthful.

At that moment, the goat arrived. Seeing that nobody was there, she too had a look around to see if she could find something to eat. She saw the cat licking his chops, quite pleased with the fine snack he had just had. She lowered her head and charged him. In order to avoid more serious consequences, the cat jumped out the window with a single "meow," and hastily ran away into the woods.

"I shall never set foot in that house again, on my honor as a cat!" he thought. "I will settle for the cock as payment for my loan."

In the meantime, the leopard had also drawn near the hunter's house and he heard the goat bleating. He slowed down, set himself on his guard, opened the door a little, and saw the goat who, ignorant of the danger, was bleating as a sign of protest at Effiong's absence. Now, given that an opportunity of this kind does not occur very often, and because there was nobody there to see him, the leopard—oh so carefully and quietly— crept up on the goat, leapt on her, and devoured her in a second.

By this time, the sun was already high in the sky, and Okun, having had lunch, placed his rifle on his shoulder and set out for his friend's house to get back the two hundred coins that he had loaned him.

As he neared the house, he heard the leopard roaring. So he stopped, leveled the rifle, and very quietly drew up to the window. Seeing the leopard, he let off a shot. The poor beast fell to the ground dead as a doornail, without even having had the satisfaction of beginning to digest the goat.

At this point, in accordance with shrewd Effiong's schemes, four of his debts had been settled: the cock had eaten the grain, the wildcat had devoured the cock, the goat had chased off the wildcat, and the goat in its turn had served as a meal for the leopard that Okun had just killed. Now only Okun remained to be dealt with, and as soon as the sound of the shot was lost in the forest, Effiong decided that the moment to show up had arrived.

As soon as he got home, he found Okun bent over the lifeless body of the leopard.

"What have you done, you wretch?" shouted Effiong, pretending to be horrified.

"But my friend," said Okun, "is this how you thank me? There was a leopard in your house, and I got rid of it for you!"

"You madman!" Effiong went on shouting. "This leopard was a very dear friend of mine and you've killed him!"

Okun tried to excuse himself, explaining that he couldn't have conceived that Effiong was friends with a leopard. But Effiong didn't want to listen to his explanations, and he threatened to report Okun to the king. Then Okun got scared because he knew that the king was not the type to overlook something like this, and he tried to calm his friend.

"Listen," Okun said, "let's do it this way: If you forget about this whole ugly affair,

I will consider your debt to be paid in full, and I'll give you the two hundred coins as a gift."

Effiong secretly rejoiced because the goal he had set for himself was about to be attained. He still pretended to resist in order to give the impression that he was not giving in immediately, but he finally accepted Okun's proposal as "partial compensation for the loss of a loved one," and then the two of them parted company for good.

And as if that weren't enough, Effiong also kept the leopard skin, which he took to the marketplace to sell in order to buy himself wine and food.

The moral of this story is very simple: "Before you lend your money, be very careful who you're giving it to!"

How the Stars Were Born

🪲 EKOI 🪲

One day, two friends named Ebopp and Mbaw went off in search of a good site to establish a farm with fine fields of grain and peanuts. They looked here and they looked there until they finally found the right place. They immediately began to fell trees and break up the soil. They worked for two days and two nights without stopping; on the third day they rested. Then at daybreak on the fourth day, they went back to work, and each of them built his own little house. And once again, they worked for two days and two nights without a break, and on the third day they rested.

But at daybreak on the fourth day, they took up their tools again and built a little temple in the middle of the farm. In two days, the little temple was finished, and on the third day they rested.

So, following the same pattern, barns, kitchens, granaries, and a well arose. When the farm was almost ready, they went to summon their wives who had remained behind in the old village, and they made merry all day to celebrate the fruits of their labor.

With their wives' help, they planted the banana seedlings, and sowed the grain and peanuts. It was long, hard work, but finally Ebopp said:

"I'm finished and so is my wife."

"I'm finished, too, and so is my wife," Mbaw echoed.

"Now all we have to do is wait for the harvest. May it be a success and may we live in comfort!" concluded Ebopp.

Nevertheless, things did not all go smoothly. One evening, when Ebopp was sitting at the table with his wife, Anwan, with the soup steaming in their bowls, someone knocked at the door. It was a messenger sent by Obassi Osaw, the leader of Anwan's village. Panting, the messenger said:

"Ebopp, I have to speak to you alone!"

So his wife left the room, and the messenger spoke:

"Be strong, Ebopp. I bring you word that your sister-in-law is dead."

Ebopp wept tears of sorrow not only for his sister-in-law, whom he loved very much, but especially for his wife, the dead woman's sister. Then he sent for his friend Mbaw to get some comfort and advice.

"I am sorry for you and for your wife, Ebopp . . . but have you thought about how we are going to bear the costs of the funeral? The farm has just been set up and the harvest is still far off."

"But, dear Mbaw, we must do everything we can, because it is my duty as a relative. How will I be able to look Chief Obassi Osaw in the face again if I don't at least have a funeral banquet?"

"You're right," said Mbaw, "we must do what is required."

Ebopp thanked his friend and told the messenger, "Go back to Obassi Osaw and tell him that I will come to his village in six days." Then he said good-bye to his friend, arranging to meet him the next day, and went to break the news to his wife.

It would take too long to describe the woman's despair at the news of her sister's death. For the next six days Anwan did not stop crying and grieving for an instant.

Nonetheless, the next day the two friends, having scraped together the few pennies in their mutual coffers, went to the city and spent all that they had to arrange the funeral banquet. Then they went back to the farm and figured out where they stood.

"So," said Ebopp, "we've spent it all and we still lack the two most important things: The palm wine and the rum for the ceremony. What are we going to do without any money?"

"Why don't you try going back to the city and making the rounds of your relatives and acquaintances? Maybe you can get a loan," Mbaw advised him.

"I'll try," replied Ebopp, and he began to travel around the city, from this one's house to that one's house, asking all his relatives and friends for loans. But with a variety of excuses, they all refused to help him. It was already nighttime when Ebopp, frustrated, began to retrace his steps.

He had just left the city and was slowly walking along the river when, in a fit of depression, he sat down on a rock, rested his chin on his hand, and began to complain.

A firefly casually alighted on his knee and Ebopp, seeking some relief, began to talk to it as if the pretty little light could actually hear him.

"My dear firefly," he said, "if you only knew how cruel the world of man is! When you're successful, everybody's your friend; but beware if things change. You lucky animals! You don't even know what falseness is!"

And he carried on in this fashion for quite some time until, to his great astonishment, he heard the firefly answer him:

"Ah, in truth, I am very sorry for you!"

"Oh river gods!" exclaimed Ebopp. "That's it! Sorrow has gone to my brain and, as if I didn't have enough problems, now I've also gone crazy! I'm hearing voices!"

"What do you mean 'crazy?'" the firefly went on. "It really is me who's talking! Listen Ebopp, I am the spirit of one of your ancestors, and it has been your great good fortune to meet me."

Ebopp rejoiced greatly at this news, and asked the firefly how he could properly honor her.

"You have an upright and generous heart, Ebopp," said the firefly. "Even in your distress, you have not forgotten the respect you owe to your ancestors. For this reason, I will give you the help that your fellow men have denied you."

The firefly's light dimmed a bit, and she handed Ebopp a sparkling little stone, saying:

"Take this. You will be able to buy all that you need and much, much more with it."

And this is why, from that day forward, only half of the firefly's body shines (excluding the head, which did not glitter even then).

Touched and happy, Ebopp clutched the little stone in his fist and ran to the farm, though not without first trying to thank the luminous little insect. But she had already taken flight. When he got back home, he summoned his wife and friend and showed them the stone. Now their worries were over.

The following day they set off for the village of Obassi Osaw, with each of them carrying a share of the supplies that they had purchased in the city for the banquet.

When they reached the entrance to the village, they separated. Anwan ran off to weep at her sister's grave, while Ebopp and Mbaw went to appear before Obassi and the elders of the tribe.

"Have you brought everything necessary for the banquet in honor of your sister-in-law?" they immediately asked.

"I only have the food with me. I will buy everything else I need here in your village," replied Ebopp.

The elders didn't say anything, but they looked at one another doubtfully. The village, and all the surrounding area, had been stricken by a grievous famine. It was almost impossible to find anything to eat or drink.

"Don't lose heart," said Mbaw to his friend. "I believe that at the sight of this beautiful little stone, the supplies will spring forth. Better still, try this: Put the stone in a mortar and crush it up really well. You will have more of it and you will be in a position to buy more stuff."

So Ebopp followed his friend's advice. He put the stone in a mortar and crushed it until it was reduced to a powder, and he saw that the result was truly extraordinary. Their eyes could scarcely tolerate the brilliant twinkling! Mbaw got his friend a little black sack, and they put the powder inside of it. Together they went off in search of everything else they needed to worthily mark the occasion.

They walked and walked until they found themselves at the edge of town in front of Effion's fine hut. Effion was one of the richest warriors in the tribe and, therefore, as always happens in times of famine, he also had one of the largest supplies of food. Ebopp said to him:

"Sell me the goatskins of wine and the barrels of rum that you have hidden away, and in exchange I will give you something that will make you so rich and powerful that all of your peers will have to bow down before you."

Effion thought about it for a minute and then replied:

"All right. But you will only get half of what you're asking, since I have to live myself, you know!"

"Agreed," said Ebopp with a hint of a smile. "Half will be enough for the funeral banquet. But listen: Don't open up the sack I'm going to give you until I have returned to my farm. And rest assured: When you open it, your fellow citizens will have to bow down before you."

And so the funeral service and the banquet took place according to custom, and everyone was pleased because absolutely nothing was lacking.

When the ceremony was over, the tribal chieftain, Obassi Osaw, went up to Ebopp and thanked him in the name of his people and begged him to stay the night. But Ebopp politely declined the invitation, and with his friend Mbaw and his wife, Anwan, he headed back home.

When they got back to their farm, Ebopp sent a messenger to Effion, the rich big shot, with the following message:

"I am back home again, and you can open the sack now."

As soon as he received the message, Effion, despite the fact that it was starting to get dark, summoned all of his fellow citizens by shouting at the top of his lungs:

"Come quick! I have something extraordinary to show you!"

"Here we are, Effion," an old warrior replied for all of them. "Now show us what you are talking about."

"I have in my possession," Effion went on, swollen with pride, "something that will make you fall on your knees before me, whether you want to or not."

Everybody looked at him with suspicion. But he swiftly took the sack out of his pocket and emptied it at their feet.

They saw a stream of brilliant light and a general "ahhh" of astonishment escaped their throats; but at that instant, a gust of wind blew. The powder flew everywhere—down the streets, onto the roofs, into the trees—covering everything with its sparkle.

Effion was very disappointed even though his fellow citizens *did* bow down before him. They had all thrown themselves to the ground in an attempt to catch some of the

miraculous powder. Only Effion remained standing straight as an arrow, struck dumb with amazement.

The children in particular distinguished themselves in picking up the shiny powder because they were faster and more nimble. Every evening, since during the day it was impossible to see the powder's twinkling, the children ran about, gradually gathering up those tiny little stars. When they caught them, they put them in a box.

Over the course of a month, the box grew so full that they had trouble closing it. But the wind brought an end to that frenzied chase. One day it blew harder than usual, knocking the box wide open, and scattering the sparkling particles into the air. They flew upward and came to a stop in the vault of the heavens, where until that time there had been nothing but darkness.

Hare's Dirty Tricks

THONGA

One day, Hare suggested to his friend Antelope that she go into partnership with him:

"How would you like to join forces and work our fields together?" he asked Antelope. "We can plant beans."

Antelope accepted and they began doing the same work. In short, Hare stole Antelope's beans and Antelope stole Hare's beans. A fine partnership indeed!

But one day Hare set a trap in his field and during the night, when Antelope was paying her usual little visit to her friend's field, she caught her leg in the trap. Then at dawn, acting as if nothing was up, Hare went into the field, and found Antelope ensnared.

"I shall have to report you to the king of the forest for what you have done!" said Hare.

"No, I beg you!" Antelope pleaded. "Set me free, and I will give you all my beans and a brand-new hoe as well."

Hare accepted, took the beans and the hoe, and went away, but not without calling the foolish Antelope a "low-down thief." A little while later, he ran into Varan, the giant lizard, comfortably stretched out in the sun next to a ditch.

"What are you doing in these parts?" asked Hare.

"I'm guarding the king's water to keep people from muddying it," replied Varan.

"And you're lying here in this scorching sun just for that? Listen to me: While you're wasting your time like a fool, your fields are going to rack and ruin. Let's go and hoe the soil instead; I can give you a hand if you like," suggested Hare.

"Hoe?" exclaimed Varan. "And how can I do that? I won't be able to stand upright on my hind legs if I have to hold the hoe in my front ones."

"What a fool you are! It's simple. I'll tie the hoe to your tail and then you can hoe as much as you choose. Come on."

Varan hesitated a bit and Hare took advantage of it. He tied the hoe to Varan's tail and the poor big lizard couldn't take another step. Then Hare quickly went over to the ditch and drank until he wasn't thirsty anymore, muddying up the water. Not satisfied with this, he ran all the way to Varan's fields and gobbled up all his peanuts.

The sun was already high in the sky and beating down hard, when Hare, having had a fine meal, came back.

"Varan! Varan! It's a good thing you stayed here! An army of grasshoppers has invaded the village and when they crossed the ditch, they muddied all the water. I've been told that they have also destroyed all of your peanut fields. It's a miracle I'm still in one piece!"

"Good grief!" exclaimed Varan. "Quick, free me from this hoe, or else I won't be able to move!"

"Sure, don't worry. But you're not going to be angry with me, are you?"

"No, no. But who told you about all these disasters?"

Hare slyly answered:

"Someone who was just passing by in a hurry . . . but don't ask questions if you want me to untie you quickly."

"All right, no questions! But hurry up, because I'm starting to feel sick."

"Such haste! Are you sure that you don't want to have a little bit to drink first? It's awfully hot out here in the sun."

"No," said Varan impatiently, "I'm fine like this. Just untie me quickly and don't worry about anything else!"

"If you don't drink, then I won't untie you," replied the spiteful Hare.

"You're really making a big deal out of this! Okay, okay, I'm very thirsty. Bring me some water, but hurry up!"

Hare ran to Varan's house, found his wooden drinking cup, drew a bit of water from the ditch, stirred the water up again, and brought it to the big lizard to drink.

"Mind now," said Hare, "if someone comes and asks you who muddied the water in the ditch, say it was an army of grasshoppers."

"Yes, yes!" Varan shouted in exasperation. "Now untie me!"

But instead of freeing him, Hare ran to summon the king and the other important members of the forest: His Majesty the Lion, His Excellency the Elephant, Her Excellency the Giraffe, and all the rest. Hare led them to Varan and when they were all gathered around the lizard, they asked him:

"Who drank from the king's ditch and muddied the water?"

"It was an army of grasshoppers," replied Varan.

But Hare quickly said:

"Liar! Look at his cup. I caught him taking a drink of water from the ditch, cool as a cucumber, instead of standing guard. So I tied him to my hoe to keep him from getting away and then ran to summon you."

"Who would ever have believed such a thing," exclaimed the king and the others. "Well done, Hare! You have unmasked the fellow who was fouling our water."

No one even listened to poor Varan's protestations. He was immediately imprisoned, put in irons, and closely guarded by the ferocious Crocodile Brothers.

But that wasn't the end of it. Hare said good-bye to everybody, put his hoe over his shoulder, and went back to look for Antelope.

He wandered around until he found Antelope, also standing guard over a stretch of water. (Water is very precious, and it must be carefully defended and watched over night and day.)

"Hare," said Antelope as soon as she saw him, "have you come because you're not satisfied with my hoe, or weren't my bean fields enough to repay you for the wrong you suffered?"

"Don't worry," replied the cunning Hare. "I'm just out for a walk. *You,* on the other hand, what are you doing standing there staring at the ditch? You haven't by any chance gone mad, have you?"

"I'm standing guard to make sure that nobody fouls the water."

Hare sniggered:

"Oh, that's a fine job indeed. While everybody else is bustling about, farming their own fields, here you are, standing there like a dunce. And what are you going to eat if there's a famine? The ditch water, maybe?"

"Well," Antelope said, faltering, "I really hadn't thought about that. . . . But anyhow, *you've* taken my beans, and you've also taken my hoe!"

"But I've already forgiven you, you silly old thing! That's all in the past now!" Hare promptly replied. "Here's the hoe. Come on, I'll help you prepare a new field."

"If that's the case, then it's a deal!" replied Antelope. "I already have just the field in mind."

But after they were hoeing for a while, Antelope said:

"I can't manage to stand up on my hind legs and hold the hoe with my front ones. That's why I was stealing your beans instead of tilling them."

"Don't lose heart," said Hare. "In just a second I'll tie the hoe to your front legs, and you'll see that you will be able to hoe splendidly."

But the experiment was not a success.

"Maybe with a lighter hoe . . ." said Hare. "Wait for me while I go to the village to look for one."

Without giving Antelope the time to respond, Hare ran off. But instead of going to the village, he went straight to the ditch where he drank his fill. And, of course, he stirred up the water and fouled it. Then he filled up a pretty yellow gourd, and when he got back to Antelope, he hid it near her.

"So," asked the naive creature, "did you find a lighter hoe?"

Hare slyly replied:

"Unfortunately I wasn't able to do anything. They told me that an army of buffalo ran through the village and destroyed it and that they also muddied all of the water in the ditch. It's incredible, isn't it?"

"The water in the ditch?" moaned Antelope. "Quick, Hare, please untie me!"

"I'll untie you, I'll untie you," said Hare. "But first you must take a drink of fresh water. You'll feel better." And he handed her the gourd.

Antelope drank without giving it much thought, and Hare ran to inform the king and the other important members of the forest. When they arrived, they saw the gourd at Antelope's feet and asked her:

"And where did this water come from?"

"Hare gave it to me," replied Antelope.

"Liar!" exclaimed Hare. "*You* got it and *you* made the water muddy. And *I,* to keep you from running away, *I* tied you to my hoe."

"What do you mean?" Antelope attempted to retort. "It was an army of buffalo that destroyed the village and muddied the water. . . ."

"What's all this nonsense about an army?" the king and the others asked. "Nobody came through here. You're lying and you will be punished."

And so Antelope, too, was imprisoned and placed under the watchful eyes of the Crocodile Brothers.

Oh, that Hare was such a rascal! Could it possibly be that everything would always go smoothly for him, and that he would never meet anyone more clever and shrewder than himself?

Then one day, Hare ran into Tortoise who was keeping an eye on the water.

"So, here you are, too, playing the fool on the bank of the ditch!" Hare said to her. "Come with me to hoe and till our fields; who do you think will help you when there's a famine? The king and his followers will soon forget your services, and they'll let you starve to death!"

"Granted you may be right," replied Tortoise, "but can you explain to me how I'm going to be able to hoe with such short legs?"

"Oh, don't worry about it, it's very simple. Let me tie your leg. . . ." But Tortoise didn't let him go on because she already knew about the trick.

"Oh no! Thanks very much," she said, "but I've already heard that little story!"

"So, you think I'm acting in bad faith!" Hare pretended to be amazed. "Do as you wish, but when the time comes and you to start to feel pangs of hunger, don't come crying to me!"

And he went away.

As a matter of fact, after a few hours Tortoise did begin to feel hungry and she didn't know what to do. Just then Hare came back.

"So," said Hare, "everything all right?"

"I have to admit it, you were right," replied Tortoise. "I'm very hungry, and I don't know what I can do about it."

Hare quickly exclaimed:

"That's why I'm here, my friend! Listen to me: Let's go into Boar's field and stuff ourselves with sweet potatoes!"

Tortoise was somewhat hesitant; she tried to object to the idea of stealing, but hunger got the better of her conscience, and she went into the sweet potato field with Hare. They stole a good heap of them that they then grilled in embers in the depths of the woods.

"Could you by any chance go and have a look to see if Boar is on our tracks?" asked Hare some time later.

"With pleasure," replied Tortoise, who still suspected something was up, "but since four eyes see better than two, why don't you come, too? I'll go this way and you can go that way."

Hare couldn't refuse, and the two of them set out, one to the right and one to the left. But as soon as she was out of Hare's sight, Tortoise turned back and hid in Hare's sack. Not long afterward, her partner also retraced his steps, and ever so swiftly filled the sack with all of the sweet potatoes.

Then, with the sack on his shoulder, Hare took flight, shouting at the top of his lungs:

"Tortoise! Tortoise! Quick, run away! Boar is coming and he's really angry! Get away! Run!"

But inside the sack, Tortoise very calmly began to eat up the potatoes. So while Hare was running, Tortoise, completely at ease, picked out the biggest and tastiest potatoes and devoured them.

After a while, Hare felt tired and hungry from all that running. When he thought that he was fairly safe, he stopped to catch his breath.

"Okay belly, here they come!" he thought happily. "The potatoes are mine!"

He made himself comfortable under a leafy tree, opened up the sack, stuck his paw in it, and began to feel around. Tortoise immediately put one of the remaining small, dried-out potatoes in Hare's paw.

"Not this one!" muttered Hare. "This one is too small!" And he stuck his paw into the sack again. Tortoise handed him another potato, another small one, just like the first one.

"Ugh! This one isn't any bigger than a hazelnut," Hare grumbled, and he put his hand back into the sack. This time he felt something big and he grabbed it. "At last!" he said, and he pulled out his paw.

Imagine Hare's face when he saw Tortoise's smiling little puss right in front of his nose!

"We reap as we sow!" exclaimed Tortoise, and making Hare put her down, she very slowly went away.

"And I even had to carry her on my back all this way!" thought Hare sadly as he made his way back home again.

Maybe you're thinking that that lesson should have been all he needed, and from that time on, he would mend his ways. Well, you are quite mistaken, because Hare was an incurable scoundrel! Once he even tried to pull Lion's leg! Can you imagine that, the king himself! Listen to what happened.

One day, His Majesty decided to summon all of the animals in the forest, one by one, because he wanted to find out which of them would be the best choice to keep watch over his peanut fields.

Each animal was examined carefully, and you won't believe this! The king chose Hare of all creatures!

"He is thievish and cunning," the king reasoned, "and he knows all the tricks. Who better than he would be able to catch a robber? After all, it takes a thief to catch a thief!"

Lion sent Hare out into the peanut fields, and for a while everything went smoothly. But not for long. Faced with so many good things, how could Hare possibly have resisted? Of course, it was risky this time . . . the king wasn't somebody to fool with . . . but after carefully considering the matter, he worked out a plan.

One morning Hare went to see the king and invited him to check how the watch was going himself. Lion agreed, and followed Hare into the fields.

After a while, Hare said:

"Your Majesty, there are quite a few thieves in your kingdom, aren't there? The devil take me if that's not true!"

"How can you say such a thing?" exclaimed the king with resentment.

"Don't get upset. Come, I'll show you the tracks of everyone who's tried to steal your peanuts. I recognize the prints and I'll give you all their names!"

His curiosity aroused, the king said:

"Okay. We'll see if you're right!"

So Hare led the king to a big banana tree and showed him many tracks under the tree, attributing them now to one animal, and then to another.

"And that's not all!" Hare said at last. "If you hide behind this tree, you'll see the thieves with your own eyes!"

Lion was quite happy with this idea, and he lay down and waited for them. In the meantime, Hare braided some branches together to make a strong rope and tied it to the tree, saying:

"While we are waiting, I'll make you a crown out of these fine banana leaves."

"Ah, thank you," replied the king, who was very vain. "That seems like an excellent idea to me."

"But first I have to comb your mane, or else your crown will be all crooked," said Hare.

"Yes, please do," said the king.

Hare immediately began to comb the lion's long mane. He gathered it into a long ponytail and then tied the ponytail back with the rope that he had fastened to the tree. Meanwhile, Lion hadn't noticed a thing.

"Watch out! Look over there," Hare suddenly exclaimed when he had finished the job. "On your feet, quickly! There's one of your subjects, and he's wolfing down your peanuts!"

Lion tried to get up, but the pain of the awful tug on his mane stopped him cold. He couldn't manage to get back up on his feet! Hare immediately called the other animals together, shouting:

"Run, run! I've found out something incredible. It's King Lion himself who's been stealing from his own fields and blaming you!"

"Look!" said Hare, after scattering a handful of peanuts at King Lion's feet. "I caught him, didn't I? He wanted to shame you so that he could have even more control over you."

Lion wasn't able to utter a word, so great was his astonishment at the absurd things

Hare was saying. But the animals took his silence as a confession. They grabbed some nice sticks and gave the poor king a sound thrashing.

Then they acclaimed Hare king of the forest, and installed him in the royal lair. He soon grew accustomed to his new position, and it seemed as if he had been a monarch since birth. He gave orders in the right style and he bossed the animals around.

However, things began to go badly when it came to important business. His subjects soon recognized he was unfit for the job, especially as a judge and ruler. So they let him know that he would have to leave office.

Hare didn't offer any resistance; quite the contrary. Instead of leaving with dignity, he thought it would be a good idea to take the whole treasury with him.

But the wheel of Hare's fortune was beginning to turn: The animals noticed his attempt to flee in time and they pursued him.

Hare ran and ran until he managed to slip into a burrow where he thought he would be safe. But with his exceptional sense of smell, Anteater found his hiding place and sounded the alarm.

They decided to drive him out by using a long, hooked stick, and after a few tries, they caught one of his paws. But Hare didn't lose heart, and playing a cunning trick, he cried:

"Come on! Pull! Pull! Anyway, you've caught the root of a tree!"

His pursuers fell for it and stopped pulling.

They let go, and then tried again, but this time they really did catch a root.

Once again Hare played a clever trick and cried:

"Ow! Ow! Please, take it easy! You'll rip off my paw if you go on pulling like that! Ow! Ow!"

Then the animals outside the den tried even harder, and pulled and pulled until the root creaked, gave, and finally ended up breaking. Immediately Hare screamed as if they were hurting him, and the animals convinced themselves that they had really fixed him this time.

"Stop!" they said. "That's enough of a lesson! From now on, he won't give us any more problems."

They plugged up the den with a big bush and went away.

Hare thought that he had fooled them yet again, but at that moment, the wind drove the bush inside the den, and shut it up like a trap.

"My God! You're suffocating me!" screamed Hare, and with a desperate effort, he pushed the bush back outside, and ran for the exit.

Nobody was there waiting for him, but he had been so frightened that he chose to take to his heels, and he never showed his face around there again.

One Hundred Head of Cattle

⚜ SWAHILI ⚜

Once upon a time, in the village of Pata, there lived a man, a woman, and their only son. All they possessed, besides the clothes on their backs and the miserable hut they lived in, was one hundred head of cattle.

The son was already a young man when his father died, so he had to tend to the cattle while his mother stayed at home to cook. But a few years later, his mother also died. And so the young man found himself all alone with the hundred animals he had inherited from his parents. A year went by, and he felt like taking a wife, so he went to see his friends in the tribe to inform them of his decision.

"A wife would certainly be useful for you," they all agreed, "but who do you intend to marry?"

"No one from our village," replied the young man. "I want a different kind of woman. Would any of you be able to take charge of choosing her? I'm young, and it's not proper for someone of my age to ask for a young girl's hand in marriage, especially if she comes from a different village."

His friends agreed that this made sense and one of them offered to act as a messenger. He left, and was back in a short time.

"I found the right woman for you in a neighboring village!" he said to the young man.

"Who is the girl?" the bridegroom asked.

"She is the only daughter of the rich man Abdallah. Her father has six thousand head of cattle."

At this news, the young man was even more convinced that he needed a wife, and he begged his friend to go back to the town to fix the terms for the marriage contract.

Abdallah listened to the messenger and replied:

"Tell the suitor that in exchange for my daughter, I want one hundred head of cattle. If the suitor accepts my proposal, there are no other obstacles."

The man said good-bye and went back to report what the girl's father had said. The young man thought about it for quite a while and then said, "One hundred head of cattle is precisely what I have. If I give them to him, what will my wife and I live on?"

"Make up your mind!" his friend urged him. "Give me your answer and I'll go and pass it on to old Abdallah. I'm committed to doing my job!"

The young man grew even more thoughtful, and began to walk back and forth, scratching his head. At last, he made a decision:

"So be it! Go and tell the old man that I accept. I will give him the hundred head of cattle he's asking for."

The friend went to tell the old man and a meeting was arranged. The young man finally saw his fiancée, who was very beautiful. He discussed the conditions of the marriage with her father. Three days later, he handed over the herd of cattle, and a month later they celebrated the marriage.

The bride went to live in her husband's village, and for a few weeks, things went smoothly: The pantry was well-supplied, and they lacked for nothing at home. But soon, their provisions ran out, and the young man said:

"Oh wife, dear wife, now we are poor. My only riches were the cattle. I milked the cows, and I tilled the fields with the oxen. I gave up the whole herd so I could have you for my wife, but I don't have anything anymore. The only thing left is for me to go and work for our neighbors; I will have to do the humblest and most tiring jobs, but at least we'll be able to eat with the little bit I'll earn."

The wife bowed her head, nodded yes, but didn't say a thing. And so every day at dawn, the young man went around to his neighbors, offering his skillful hands and strong arms in exchange for a bit of milk, a small bag of grain, or a little piece of meat. Sometimes he milked the cows, chopped the wood, or fixed a roof; often he fetched water from the river for the women who were home alone, but they paid him little or nothing.

In the meantime, the son of one of the most important figures in the village, a good-looking youth, had laid his eyes on the pretty foreigner and had gotten it into his head that he wanted to court her. So every day after her husband had gone out to look for work, the young man showed up and began to wander around near the house, trying to strike up a conversation with her. The woman pretended nothing was wrong; she didn't dare talk to her husband about it, for fear that he would stay home and lose even that little bit of work he managed to get.

Six months and a day went by, and old Abdallah decided to pay a visit to his daughter and her husband. Without announcing his visit, he set off on his journey.

When he reached his son-in-law's house, he knocked on the door, and his daughter came to open it. What a surprise!

"Luckily, the house is in order and I'm wearing my last new dress," thought the poor young thing when she saw him. Hiding her embarrassment, she made her father comfortable, and offered him some fresh fruit.

"So my daughter," said the old man, "how are you? Are you happy with your husband?"

"Oh yes, father," she replied a bit hesitantly. But she couldn't manage to hold back her despair, and pretending to get water to make the tea, she locked herself in her room and burst into a flood of tears.

"And now what?" she asked herself in despair. "There's nothing to eat in the house, but I have to at least invite my father to dinner!"

As she was trying to think of a solution, she saw the young man who had been trying to court her through the window. So she dried her tears, tidied herself up as best she could, and went out by the back door, pretending to pass him by chance.

"Please excuse my insistence and my craziness," he said to her, "but ever since I first saw you, I don't sleep and I don't eat anymore. My father is rich. Leave that poor beggar and run away with me. You'll see that I'll be able to make you happy and I will treat you like a queen."

The girl flirted with him a bit and then replied:

"It was a mistake to marry a man who can't even support himself. If your love is sincere, take me away from here. I'm tired of living in poverty without ever eating enough or being able to buy myself a new dress."

"At last!" rejoiced the young man. "Let's go this very day, or better still, right now!"

"Just a moment!" she went on. "Wait a second. My father just arrived to visit me, and I haven't seen him for such a long time. I need to make him a nice dinner, but as I've already told you, I don't have anything to offer him. Go and get me a nice piece of meat to put on the table so I won't look shabby. Afterward, rest assured, I will come with you."

"All right," said the young man, beaming. "You will have your meat in an instant!" And a little while later, he came back with an entire quarter of beef.

"Take it, and remember your promise," he said to her.

"Don't worry," replied the girl, and grasping the huge piece of beef, she went back inside to cook.

By now it was dinnertime, and her husband came back home after having done a few little jobs for a neighbor. When he saw his father-in-law, he was frightened! He really didn't need this! What could they offer him? He would surely notice what misery his daughter was living in. But he managed to control himself, and acting as if everything was just fine, he greeted his father-in-law with affection. The two of them chatted for a little while, and then the young man, with some excuse, went into the kitchen to see his wife.

"You're cooking?" he asked, astonished. "But there wasn't anything in the house!"

"Husband, I found some meat. . . ." she replied hesitantly.

"What do you mean 'found'? Who gave it to you?"

"Well, now don't get angry, but I appealed to our neighbors' kind hearts. I explained that my father was here for dinner, but that I didn't have anything to give him, and so they gave me this meat."

The young man didn't say another word. He bowed his head and felt dreadfully embarrassed: His neighbors were giving him charity—so this is what he had been reduced to!

Seeing him so depressed, his wife tried to comfort him.

"Cheer up," she said. "Don't think about it. We'll repay them for the meat and then we won't be under any obligations. But now, go and keep my father company. Dinner will be ready very soon. Sit down and I'll serve it."

Meanwhile, seeing as the girl hadn't shown up, the waiting suitor moved closer to the front door, hoping to see her and be able to signal to her. But at some point as he was walking back and forth in front of the open door, the husband saw him. And recognizing him as the son of one of the people who gave him work now and then, he greeted him and invited him to come inside.

Unable to find a good excuse for declining, the young man was forced to accept the invitation, and he sat down at the table with the others. And so the three of them—father, husband, and suitor—began to politely speak as if everything were quite normal.

A little while later, the meat, done to a turn, arrived on the table, and the girl, not in the least bit fazed by the strange trio, smiled affectionately and said:

"Dinner is served, you foolish men!"

There was a moment of embarrassment, and a shadow of suspicion hovered in the air.

The father was the first to break the silence that followed his daughter's words, asking:

"What reason do you have for calling me a fool?"

"Father," replied the young woman, "don't be annoyed; first eat and be merry, then I'll explain why I called you a fool."

But her father replied:

"Oh no! Let's first hear why I am a fool. I've lost my appetite."

So his daughter fearlessly spoke her mind:

"Father, you are foolish because you gave away something precious in exchange for something so small."

"I?" said her father. "And what is this precious thing that I have given away for nothing?"

"You don't get it? I'm talking about myself."

"That you are precious to me is true, but explain yourself better. . . ."

"It's simple. You had no children other than me, and yet you gave me up for a hundred head of cattle, even though your herds amounted to over six thousand head. Were those miserable hundred head worth more than me perhaps?"

Her father felt himself flush with shame and said:

"My daughter, you are right! I have indeed been a fool."

And now it was the husband's turn to ask:

"And why did you also call me a fool?"

His wife looked at him and replied:

"You are even more foolish than my father. You inherited a few cattle from your parents and you gave them away so you could have *me*. If you had chosen a girl from your own village, it wouldn't have cost you anything, but you wanted a foreigner and so you have reduced yourself to poverty. Not only that, you have also reduced me to poverty because we don't even have enough to eat every day. If you had at least kept a few head of the cattle, you would not be forced to play the servant to others now."

And the husband had to acknowledge that his wife was right: He *had* been more foolish than his father-in-law.

Even the young man, who wished to take her away from her husband wanted to know why he had been called as a fool. And immediately the young woman responded:

"You are more foolish than my father and my husband put together. That's for sure!"

"What on earth do you mean?" he exclaimed resentfully.

"For a miserable quarter of a steer, you wanted to get what had been bought and sold

for one hundred head of cattle. Aren't you perhaps more foolish than my father and my husband?"

The young suitor blushed with shame and fear, and decided it was best to leave before the conversation got too clear . . . and before the husband thrashed him.

The bride's father went back to his village, but he hastened to send back the one hundred head of cattle to his son-in-law, with an additional two hundred to win their forgiveness.

And so the young couple was rich once more, and they lived together happily for many, many years.

Two Strange Villages

✦ HAUSA ✦

A long, long time ago, there lived a woman who had two daughters of marriageable age. The days went by, and at last the woman found husbands for her two daughters, but each of the two suitors had something peculiar about him. One came from a village where nobody was allowed to sleep; the other from a place where nobody was allowed to eat. Don't ask me how this was possible. Perhaps the two villages were victims of a spell or some other kind of devilry, but the fact is that in one of them, people didn't sleep, and in the other, people didn't eat.

The woman didn't give too much weight to these unusual circumstances, and she married her daughters to the young men she had chosen. The first one brought his wife to the village where nobody slept; the second one brought his to the one where nobody ate.

The elder one settled down in a lovely house with many servants ready to obey her every command. She lacked for nothing, except for the pleasure of sleep. Night after night of not sleeping a wink left her overwhelmed by fatigue; she became irritable and cranky and she couldn't manage to control her nerves anymore. She tried to make her husband understand that sleep was absolutely essential for her. But he didn't understand and he looked at her with irritation, mixed with a bit of fear.

So the daughter decided to write her mother a note in which she wrote:

"Mama, I am well but I would like to have you as our guest for a few days."

As soon as she read the message, the woman realized that something was wrong. She made some sweets to bring to her daughter, put on her best dress, and left.

After a day and a night, she reached the village where people never slept. They all made her a hearty welcome and prepared a banquet in her honor.

"We welcome you," her son-in-law said in one of the many toasts, "and may you never sleep!"

At this wish, all the guests applauded; only the woman was puzzled.

And her daughter whispered to her:

"Mama, don't eat or drink too much, otherwise you'll get tired and run the risk of falling asleep! Afterward, I'll come to you and explain things better."

The party ended, the guests left, and the mother listened to her daughter's tirade: She loved her husband, but she couldn't stand this life anymore. She needed to sleep, but she feared that if she did, she would offend her new people, and perhaps even be driven out.

The mother realized that the situation was rather unusual, but she didn't know what to do yet. Somehow, she calmed her daughter down and then went to lie down. But the whole affair continued to worry her so much that she couldn't manage to fall asleep. And that was a lucky thing, because then she didn't offend anybody.

At the break of dawn, her daughter went to draw water from the well; as she went out, she said to her mother:

"I've put the milk on the fire; keep an eye on it while I'm away."

The mother sat down near the fireplace, and lo and behold, the gentle warmth of the fire and her fatigue from her sleepless night began to take effect: She started to nod her head and yawn. Another few minutes, and sleep got the upper hand. She stretched out in front of the fireplace and immediately fell asleep.

At that precise moment, a neighbor arrived to ask for a little milk. She entered, called out, went over to the fireplace, and saw the sleeping woman.

"Help! Help!" she cried, tearing at her hair. "What a calamity! The poor woman is dead!"

A great uproar ensued: This one running around over here, that one crying over there, somebody beating a drum to summon the entire village, and somebody organizing the funeral ceremony!

Her daughter also heard all the racket and immediately ran home. As soon as she came inside, she realized what had happened and shouted:

"Quiet! Quiet! My mother isn't dead, she's sleeping!"

There was a heavy silence, and all eyes rested on the daughter.

"Yes," she resumed, "sleeping is normal for us. Sleep is not death. Look!" And she shook her mother hard.

The mother awoke with a start and sat right up, rubbing her eyes. They all looked at her in fear, thinking that she had come back to life; but between yawns the woman explained:

"My dear son-in-law, relatives, and good friends, sleep is necessary and it's good for you. Therefore, do not be afraid of sleep. It's a natural thing."

Then they were all ashamed of their silly fear, and on that day, the whole village finally started to learn how to sleep.

At the same time in the village where people were not allowed to eat, the second daughter had also settled down in a beautiful house filled with servants ready to satisfy her every desire. Everything was very beautiful and everybody loved her. There was just one

drawback: No food—not in the morning, not at noontime, not at suppertime . . . and believe me that's no small thing.

The girl began to feel exhausted, and she tried to explain her needs to her husband, but he didn't understand because he didn't even know what eating was.

So the second daughter sent her mother a note that read:

"Mama, I'm enjoying myself very much here, but I would like you to be our guest for a few days."

The mother, who had just come back from her visit with her elder daughter, immediately sensed that something was wrong; she made some sweets, put on her best dress, and left.

She walked for a day and a night, and at last she reached the village where nobody

ever ate. Everybody welcomed her with great displays of joy, and arranged a dance in her honor.

"Let's have a cheer for my wife's mother, and may she never ever know the taste of food!"

This was followed by an explosion of cheers, salutes, and good wishes from all sides, but the woman didn't appear to be very happy with it all. Her daughter noticed this and whispered to her:

"Mama, smile and act as if nothing's wrong. Come to me later on, and I'll explain everything."

The dance came to an end, the exhausted guests left, and the mother listened to her daughter's complaints: She loved her husband, and she understood the customs of the village, but if she didn't eat at least once a day, her handsome husband would soon be a handsome widower.

The mother tried to calm her daughter down. She accompanied the girl to her bedroom, bid her good night, and then went back to her own room. She began to look for a solution to her daughter's problem, and finally she had an idea. After dark she went into a field of wild pumpkins, gathered the biggest and ripest ones, and went back to the house.

She worked all night, and by the morning, she had made more than a hundred bowls of steaming hot soup that she then set out on the veranda.

When everything was ready, she went to summon her daughter and said:

"Come, breakfast is already on the table."

"But mama," exclaimed her daughter, "you must know that people don't eat here!"

"Indeed I do!" retorted her mother, and she pushed her daughter out onto the veranda.

The two women sat down and began to eat with great gusto.

At that moment a little boy came up to them in tears because his bow had broken. The two women comforted him and cuddled him. Then, almost without knowing what they were doing, they began to offer him a few spoonfuls of hot soup.

The little boy was quite astonished by this novelty. He looked at the strange thing with amazement, tasted the soup, and discovered that it was good. The women poured him some milk, and he found that that was good, too. The little boy stopped his whimpering, clapped his hands with pleasure, and asked for another helping.

As he was greedily gulping down his second bowl of soup, who should arrive but his father! Seeing his son eating, the father first turned pale, and then asked in alarm:

"My son! What have these witches done to you? Now you are going to die!"

"No!" the mother said. "People die from *not* eating."

The father's cries drew everybody in the village, and, with worried looks, they gath-

ered round the greedy little fellow. The son-in-law was also there, and he couldn't manage to hide either his rage or his shame.

"My dear son-in-law, relatives, and good friends," the woman said. "Come here and do as this innocent babe, who discovered all by himself that eating is something natural and instinctive."

Then they all felt ashamed of their foolishness, and they sat down at the table close to the two women in order to learn about the custom of eating.

And from that day on, they never even skipped their afternoon snack.

The Eagle and the Baby

⚇ BAILA ⚇

A long, long time ago, there lived a woman who had a baby boy. Since she went to work in the fields every day and didn't know whom to leave him with, she always brought him with her. Every day when she got to the fields, she settled the baby in the shade and nursed him. Then she grabbed her hoe and began her difficult labors.

One day, even though she had nursed the baby for a good while and found him a lovely little spot in the shade of a banana tree, he began to cry and would not stop. The mother tried to soothe him, and managed to calm him down for a little while, but as soon as she went back to work, the little one burst into another fit of tears.

At that moment, an eagle came down from the sky and landed right beside the baby. She caressed him with her feathers and tickled him with her beak until she made him smile. Then when she saw the mother approaching with her hoe raised threateningly, she flew away.

The mother clasped the baby tight to her breast and went back to the village.

She didn't say anything to her husband about this extraordinary incident for fear that he would not believe her. So she made supper as usual, nursed her little son, and went to bed.

The next morning, the woman went back to work in the fields, taking the baby with her. As always, she settled her son in the shade, nursed him, and then taking up her hoe, she began to work.

But after a little while, the little one began crying and screaming. And lo and behold, the eagle came down from the sky again and began caressing him with her feathers and tickling him with her beak.

This time the woman's surprise was greater than her fear.

"What an astonishing thing!" she exclaimed. "Instead of harming my son, that eagle is caressing him and soothing him; and the baby has calmed down."

Then the woman took the baby and immediately went back to the village.

As soon as her husband saw her coming back so early and in such a rush, he asked her what had happened.

"Something amazing!" said the woman, her voice breaking with emotion.

"Nothing out of the ordinary ever happens here. What on earth could this miracle be?!" said the husband.

"Both yesterday and today, while I was tilling in the fields, an eagle came down. . . ."

"So?" her husband interrupted. "It's not such an extraordinary thing to see an eagle."

"Listen husband, that's not it . . . it's that the baby was crying and crying. I was about to go and see what was the matter with him, when out of the clear blue sky, an eagle came down, landed next to him, caressed him with her wings, and touched him with her beak; the baby immediately calmed down."

"Wife," her husband said harshly, "what's this nonsense you're telling me? Nothing like that has ever happened, as far as anyone can remember. Keep your tall tales to yourself!"

So the woman hung her head and didn't say anything more. She picked up the baby again, put the hoe back over her shoulder, and went back to the fields to work.

She lay her son down in the shade, nursed him, and then left to go and till. And after a bit, the baby once again started to cry.

Then the woman thought, "I'm going to run home right now and get my husband so he can see this with his own eyes!" And she went back to the village with the baby.

When she saw her husband outside their hut, busily sharpening arrows, she shouted to him, "Come quickly! You decide whether I've told you the truth!"

Taken by surprise, the husband instinctively grabbed his bow and arrows and followed his wife. And as soon as they reached the field, the woman said:

"Hide behind those bushes and don't move; I'll lay the baby down over there in the shade."

Immediately the little one, feeling lonely, began to cry and scream until the eagle appeared and caressed him with her wings and tickled him with her beak.

But seeing this, the father became terribly alarmed. He drew his bow, took aim, and let fly an arrow. But by chance, at that very moment, the eagle had moved to the side, and the arrow meant for her struck the baby.

And this, the elders tell us, is how the first murder occurred.

The eagle immediately took flight, saying:

"Man, and with you all men who are and those who are yet to come: Just as I came down to comfort your child, so may my curse come down on you. You have killed your own flesh and blood and one of your fellow creatures will kill you; thus men will kill one another forever."

And unfortunately, her curse continues to this day.

Ngomba and Her Basket

 B A K O N G O

One day, at dawn's first light, four little girls decided to go fishing in the big river. One of them was Ngomba, a poor, sickly little girl covered with sores—the poorest girl in the whole village. The four little girls set out, but after a few steps, the other three turned to Ngomba and said:

"Go home, you ragamuffin. You're not like us. Go home!"

"No," Ngomba quickly replied, "I will not go back. I want to catch a fish for my mother, too!"

"You?!" her companions exclaimed in chorus. "What do you expect to catch, as sick as you are? Go away, go back to the village!"

Ngomba felt tears rise to her eyes, but she remained silent. She let the others go on ahead, and she started walking along the route by the lake. She had no intention of giving up her fishing. She walked and walked until she reached the bank of the big river where she made herself a fishing pole, and began to fish.

"I am just a poor little girl . . ."

she sang as she threw in her hook; and immediately a fish bit. She put it in her basket and started to sing again:

"Nobody cares about me,"

another fish ended up in her basket.

"The others said, 'Oh, go away,' "

another fish ended up in her basket.

"And I'm all alone as can be!"

and another fish ended up in her basket.

Just then a bandit happened to be passing by. He heard the little girl's song and set about spying on her. Noticing how many fish she had managed to catch, he came out of the bush and approached her.

"What are doing around here all by yourself?"

"Can't you see?" replied Ngomba. "I'm fishing. But who are you?"

"What the devil?! I am a bandit and everyone is afraid of me!" he answered back.

"Oh bandit, I beg you, don't kill me!" pleaded the child. "I may be sick, but I'm good at fishing; just watch how it's done!" And she threw her hook back in and started singing again:

"Now this man wants to kill me,"

a fish bit and ended up in her basket.

"Nobody cares about me,"

another fish ended up in her basket.

"I weep and beg him for mercy,"

another fish ended up in her basket.

" 'No mercy for you,' says he!"

and another fish ended up in her basket.

Admiring the child's incredible ability, the amazed bandit said to her, "Don't be afraid. Now you are going to come with me."

But Ngomba replied, "No, I can't. I have to bring these fish to my mama."

"Either you come with me or I'll kill you!" exclaimed the bandit. So the child again threw in her hook and sang:

"This bandit threatens to slay me,"

a fish bit and ended up in her basket.

"Nobody cares about me,"

another fish ended up in her basket.

"But leave these fish for my mommy,"

another fish ended up in her basket.

"And I'll get you some more, you'll see!"

and another fish ended up in her basket.

The bandit thought this over for a few minutes and then said:

"All right! We'll take the fish to your mother; but then you will come and live with me. I will heal your sores and you will be treated with the greatest respect; then when you grow up, I will marry you."

The child didn't know what to say. She merely realized that for the moment her life was safe, and so she did what the bandit wanted. They gave the fish to her mother and went away together to another village.

Ngomba recovered from her terrible illness. She grew up in great comfort, surrounded by all the attentions that the bandit had promised her, and thus reached the age when she was to marry.

But Ngomba had no intention of marrying the bandit, and she devised a plan to free herself from him. She assembled her most faithful servants and sent them into the forest every day to gather the toughest palm leaves they could find. Then she dried them in the sun in a clearing far away from the village. And when she thought she had enough of them, she built an enormous basket, similar to the one she used to go fishing.

The days passed and the bandit didn't suspect a thing, even though he often smelled a strong odor of palm juice in the air and couldn't figure out where it was coming from. He continued his life of robberies, attacks, and murders, and constantly thought about his wedding day.

At last the basket was finished—as was the time that Ngomba had to complete her plan. That same morning before he went out, the bandit had said to her:

"Get dressed up. We're getting married at noon."

So Ngomba and her servants carried the basket to the edge of a cliff. They jumped in the basket and started to rock it, until, unbalancing it, they managed to make it fall into the void.

But the wind caught it and held it up with its strong, invisible hand. And Ngomba sang:

"On basket, homeward! Do as I say,"

and the basket turned in the direction of Ngomba's mother's house.

"Fly swiftly and take me away,"

and the basket moved.

"Far away, as fast as you can,"

and the basket took off like a shot.

"Quick, quick, away from that man!"

and the basket flew and flew.

But it just so happened that they ended up passing over the bandit's head. He was hiding on the branch of a tree, waiting to attack some poor passerby. The bandit said "Oh!" and was sorry that his future bride wasn't there to see such a marvel: An enormous basket suspended in midair, peacefully going on its way!

At that very moment, the strange aircraft lost a bit of height and almost grazed his head. Then the bandit saw that the basket was full of people that he knew quite well, and in the midst of them was his bride. Recovering from his astonishment, the bandit set off in pursuit, leaping from tree to tree until he saw the basket disappear in the direction of Ngomba's village.

Meanwhile, after flying over the group of huts a couple of times, the basket landed right in front of the girl's old house.

Ngomba got down and ran to hug her mother, who didn't recognize her at first. But

after looking into her eyes, she realized that this was her sick little girl who had been taken away by the bandit such a long time ago. How she had grown! And how healthy and beautiful she looked!

Just then the bandit arrived at a run, yelling for his bride, howling, and threatening to destroy everything! So the old woman spoke up and said to him:

"It's true that my daughter owes much to you because you cured all her ills. We are grateful to you, but you cannot demand that Ngomba stay with you if she doesn't want to."

"Old woman," said the enraged bandit, "don't talk nonsense! The girl is mine! I healed her and I'm keeping her!"

Then the mother realized that to get the better of a bully you had to use his own tactics. She told the bandit to wait until the evening to take Ngomba away, and in the meantime she had a big pit dug in her kitchen. She put the big pot that she used for making soap in the pit, and filled the pot with boiling water. Then she covered the pit with a mat of leaves and branches and invited the bandit to dinner.

It is easy to imagine how this story ends: The bandit falls into the pot of boiling water and gets boiled up. It is to be hoped that he realized in the end that if you do someone a good turn, it doesn't mean that you should then make them a slave to your wishes.

How the Cracks in the Tortoise's Shell Came to Be

BAILA

Now I have to tell you that Mr. Tortoise, happily married to Mrs. Tortoise, had a very good friend, Mr. Vulture, who very often came to pay them a visit. And he always brought some sort of gift for the lady and something tasty for the husband.

Tortoise would have liked to repay these kind visits, but how could he if he didn't have wings? Vulture lived way up in the mountains, and for Tortoise, getting that far was a hopeless goal.

One day he went to his wife and said to her:

"My dear wife, you too have probably been thinking that if we don't return Vulture's visits at least once, we will seem very impolite."

"You're right," replied the lady, "but how can we? Vulture will understand. We can't fly, not unless we sprout wings!"

"Don't be so silly!" exclaimed Mr. Tortoise. "If nature had wanted to give us wings instead of shells, we'd be birds and not tortoises."

"Oh really? Are you sure about that?" replied his wife. "But then how do you plan to resolve this problem?"

"I have to find a way. . . ." said Tortoise thoughtfully.

"Well, when you find one, let me know!" concluded his wife, shaking her head.

A day and a night went by, and at dawn of the following day, Tortoise, quite pleased with himself, announced to his wife:

"I've got it! I have a magnificent idea! Listen: Vulture is supposed to come and see us today. Now, your job is to wrap me up really well in these palm leaves, and when our guest arrives, give him the parcel and tell him that it's some tobacco that we need to swap for some corn. I'll take care of the rest."

The wife did as her husband told her and wrapped him up like a great big parcel.

Vulture came to call on them, and seeing that Tortoise wasn't home, he asked the wife:

"And where is your husband, Mrs. Tortoise?"

"He had to go and see some relatives, and he won't be back for a week. It's a fine mess!"

"A mess? But why? A week goes by very quickly!" said Vulture.

"It's a mess, I tell you, Mr. Vulture," she insisted, "because he's gone off and left me without even a kernel of corn. I would go and get me some if I could swap this parcel of tobacco for it, but there's no corn to be found in these parts. As you know, I am too slow to make a long trip."

"A fine mess indeed. . . . I understand your concern!" said Vulture. Then after some thought, he added:

"But if you like, I can get it for you. There's extra corn from the crops in my part of the country!"

"Oh, how kind of you, Mr. Vulture! If it's really not too much trouble, I accept your courteous offer with pleasure."

"Don't mention it! It will be a pleasure!"

So Vulture grasped the parcel of tobacco in his claws, with Mr. Tortoise inside, and flew off toward his nest.

But as he was flying, he heard a voice coming from the parcel:

"Hey, old fellow! It's me, your old friend Tortoise. See, I've managed to come all the way up here to pay you a visit!"

In his amazement, Vulture dropped the parcel. It crashed to the ground, and Tortoise's shell was completely covered in cracks from the fall.

From that day on, both Vulture and Tortoise decided to stay at home, but those cracks in the tortoise's shell never healed. And they're still there today.

The Grateful Serpent

 **NUER**

One day, a man came upon two serpents fighting with one another. He drew near and saw that one of them was about to get the worst of it. The man was moved to pity, and using a stick, he separated the two opponents. He threatened the bigger one, which took off as fast as it could, and touched the other one with the end of his stick to see if it was still alive.

"Thank you ever so much!" the serpent exclaimed. "Were it not for you, I would be dead by now! To show you my gratitude, I will cast a spell on you that will allow you to understand everything that animals say."

"Are you serious?" asked the man.

"Of course! You will know what the mosquito, the mouse, and even the cow is saying. But keep this to yourself!"

This gift pleased the man. The two said a friendly good-bye, and then each went his own way.

That evening before going to bed, the man carefully closed all the doors and windows.

A little while later, a mosquito tried to get in through the door. It tried the windows next, but couldn't even find a crack to slip through. Then, thoroughly enraged, it buzzed:

"Foul curses on this place! This house is sealed up tighter than a coffin! How can I get in there?"

Inside the house, the man understood the buzzing and began to laugh.

"Hey! Why are you laughing?" his wife asked, turning over to look at him.

"Oh, it's nothing, it's nothing!" replied the man, stifling another laugh. And they went back to sleep.

Not long afterward, a mouse also tried to get in. It checked the door and the windows and they seemed impossible to get through. The mouse thought for a few minutes and then made straight for the roof. It found an opening between the planks and stole into the house. The mouse explored all the rooms, looking for cheese; but after rummaging here, and rummaging there, it found there was no cheese anywhere. Then it squeaked in annoyance:

"Curses! What kind of a house is this? There's not even a crumb of cheese rind here!"

Lying in bed, the man heard the mouse, understood its squeaking, and laughed heartily.

"What's there to laugh about now?" asked his wife.

"Oh, nothing at all, really!" replied her husband, trying hard to restrain himself.

The night passed, and dawn came. Just as he did every other morning, the man went into the cowshed, untied the cattle, and led them to pasture. The cows were talking to each other, and the man listened to them with great interest.

Then it was time to milk the cows, and his wife arrived with the pail and stool. The largest of the cows mooed:

"Girls, here comes that woman to steal our milk!" Hearing this and understanding it, the man laughed heartily.

"Laughing again?" said his wife angrily.

"No . . . well . . ." said the husband, but he didn't have time to come up with a believable excuse, and at the same time the cow started mooing again:

"Not today, my dear! Today I'm keeping my milk for my little calf," and she slowly trotted farther away from the woman.

And the man, who heard this and understood it, couldn't manage to restrain himself and he laughed again.

"Well!!!" exploded his wife. "Who do you think you're making fun of?"

"Oh, my sweet little wife, nobody, nobody!" he said, trying to calm her down.

"You're behaving like a fool!" she said. And taking up her pail and stool, she went back home.

In the evening, the woman came back to milk the cows, but she got only a few drops.

"Husband, this cow is not cooperating!" she exclaimed.

"Are you going to take care of nursing my calf?" mooed the cow mischievously.

The man doubled up with laughter.

"Oh! So you're laughing, huh!" shrieked the woman, angered. "You're making fun of me, and you don't care a thing about me!"

And once again the cow mooed:

"And maybe he has his reasons!"

And out came another laugh from the husband who once again couldn't manage to restrain himself.

"If that's the way it is," said his wife at that point, "I'm going to ask the wise men of the village to meet at our house tonight. I will tell them my problem and ask for a divorce!"

The husband couldn't find the strength to reply, choked with laughter as he was, and this certainly did not serve to calm his wife's anger.

In the evening, the wise men came, sat down around the fire, and said to the woman:

"You sent for us. What is this about?"

"My husband is laughing at me for no reason at all. We go to bed and he laughs; he

takes the cattle to graze and he laughs; I go to milk them and he laughs. I don't like to be made fun of!"

The wise men looked at each other, nodded in agreement, and said to the husband:

"Explain to us why you are laughing at your wife."

"No, wise men, I am not laughing at her," said the husband.

"Then who are you laughing at?" they asked.

"I am not allowed to say that," replied the man.

"You don't mean to pull our legs, too, do you? Speak!" commanded the wise men.

So the man decided to tell them about the grateful snake who had given him this magic gift.

"In short," he concluded, "I can hear and understand everything that the animals are saying."

The wise men looked at each other and shook their heads. The case was crystal clear: The man had gone crazy. Then they left the room to speak with one another and come to a decision.

"Woman," they said when they returned, "as of this day, you are free. You are granted a divorce because your husband has gone mad."

The woman began to cry, and her husband tried to explain again how things were. But the wise men's verdict could not be appealed, and it was no use trying to make them change their minds.

The marriage was ended, the people of the village sympathized with the unhappy couple, and the man retired to a deserted spot to avoid causing more trouble for his former wife. He had been living there for some time when he met the serpent again.

"Man," the serpent said to him, "it is a pleasure to see you again. What on earth are you doing around these parts?"

"If you only knew!" he replied, sighing. "I had to reveal your great gift to me to my village, and they all thought I was crazy. I lost my wife, and I had to leave the village. No one can say that you've brought me luck!"

"How stupid you men are!" exclaimed the serpent. "You don't see what's true and you take appearances for fact. Listen: The people who call you crazy are crazier than you. Don't think about them anymore. You lost a wife who didn't understand you, and with her, the trouble of supporting her. You have escaped the stupidity of your fellow men and you had faith in what you believed. Who could be happier than you? Be merry, and may the gods protect you!"

"It's true!" thought the man. "The serpent is right: I am a free man and a lucky one!" And whistling happily, he headed for a field of corn to listen to the conversation of the free and lucky birds.

ASHANTI *(Asante)*

The Ashanti live in central Ghana. Ashanti women frequently carry Akuaba dolls. These are magic wooden dolls that women put in the backs of their skirts to guarantee that they have healthy, beautiful babies.

BAILA *(Ila)*

The rainbow in Africa is viewed as strange and dangerous. The people do not look upon it as a thing of beauty, but rather with awe, as they associate it with something magical. For example, the Baila of Zambia point at the rainbow with a pestle to drive it away; they believe that at the rainbow's end there awaits a ferocious ram burning with fire.

BAKONGO *(Bakango)*

The Bakongo live near the mouth of the Congo. Although converted to Christianity, the Bakongo are able to blend European ideas with their Congo ancestry. For example, their crosses do not only represent Christian beliefs. To the Bakongo, the transverse beam of the cross shows the border of this world and the afterlife, and the upright beam shows the path of power between the two worlds.

BAVENDA *(Bawenda, Vhavenda, Venda)*

The Bavenda in southern Africa used divining bowls. These bowls, when filled with water and many other objects, are used to discover what the future holds. The divining bowls of the Bavenda are decorated with patterns and pictures around the sides and a glossy, brightly colored shell in the middle. This shell represents the spirits.

EFIK-IBIBIO

The Efik live in southern Nigeria, and the Ibibio live in southeast Nigeria. They believe that good and evil are inherent in nature, and this belief has led them to create ugly masks used to ward off the evil forces.

EKOI

One form of art practiced by the Ekoi, who lived near the Efiks, was stone sculpture. There is not a great deal of stone sculpture in Africa, and it is mostly found in Sierra Leone, Nigeria, and the Congo. They usually used soft stone, although quartz and granite were also used.

HAUSA

In Africa, pottery, baskets, beaded objects, and beautiful, rich fabrics of all kinds are given as gifts to show love, affection, and friendship. Among the Hausa, who live in northern Nigeria and southern Niger, the decorated *calabash* (gourd) is given to mark major occasions in life, such as engagements, marriages, and births. Many calabashes bear great, detailed designs of snakes, men, or gods.

KIKUYU *(Gikuyu)*

The Kikuyu live in central and southern Kenya. They have a myth that at the beginning of the world, the creator made a great mountain as a symbol of his strength and power, as well as a resting place for himself. People would turn toward it and lift up their hands during prayer and offer sacrifices there. The Kikuyu named the mountain *Kere Nyanga,* or Mountain of Brightness. The Europeans call this same mountain Mount Kenya.

KRACHI *(Kratyi)*

The Krachi lived in Togo. They liked to farm, and some of the crops that they grew included cotton, cow peas, flute pumpkins, gourds, millet, oil palms, okra, sesame, and sorghum.

MASAI *(Maasai)*

The Masai live in Kenya and parts of Tanzania. Having children is very important to the Masai as it represents the preservation of the life force. To guarantee this continuation, they sometimes perform a ceremony under an ancient tree. In the ceremony they strike the tree with a stick, and if a sweet, milky liquid is released, it means a life of plenty and happiness.

MBUNDU *(A-Mbundu, Kimbundu)*

The Mbundu, a part of the Bantu people, live in southern and central Angola. The Mbundu animal tales, like other African animal tales, amuse, give explanations, and often comment on human faults and values. As such, they show what is believed to be good and proper behavior.

NUER

The Nuer of Sudan believe in many gods and, like many other African peoples, they believe in witchcraft. The most popular image of the witch in Africa is that of a cruel woman who works at night, killing for viciousness or for simple fun. The Nuer believe that witchcraft has both good and bad possibilities, and that it turns evil only in the hands of wicked people.

SWAHILI *(Soahili, Suaheli, Wasuaheli)*

Swahili means "the people of the coast." They inhabit the coast and islands of eastern Africa, from Somalia to Mozambique. They are mainly Muslim, and they speak the Bantu language known as *Kiswahili*. Kiswahili has become the official language of much of the East Africa and the Congo area.

THONGA *(Bathonga)*

The Thonga of South Africa live in small towns, called *kraals*, inhabited by members of a large, extended family. Their homes are straw-thatched cone-shaped huts—the walls of which are made of branches and twigs covered with clay—usually built around a cattle corral.

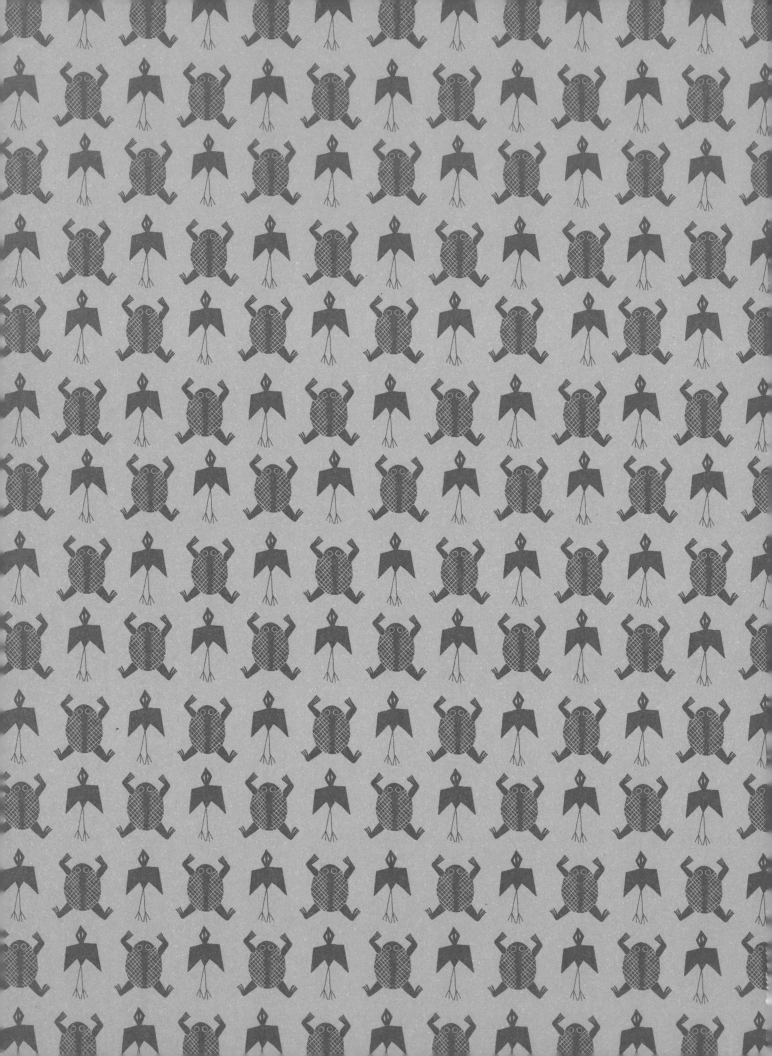